COMMUNICATIONS CABLING

JAMES ABRUZZINO

Second Edition

The author has not received any compensation from manufacturers for the display of equipment in this book. Appearance of a product in this book does not imply any endorsement.

First Edition November 1998. Revised First Edition May 1999. Second Edition July 2000. ISBN 0-9671630-0-5

Disclaimers

Every effort has been made to provide complete, accurate and current information. Due to the dynamic nature of the communications industry, information is subject to change at any time without notice. Neither the author, publisher, nor distributors may be held responsible for damages relating to any information contained or not contained in this book.

Trademarks

All Trademarks are the property of their respective owners.

National Electrical Code® and *NEC*® are registered trademarks of the National Fire Protection Association, Inc., Quincy, MA 02269.

Production Credits

Editing & Technical Review: Jason Gardiner, David Hensel, Rob Mullins, Mike Sandman

I would like to express special thanks to my family (for their editing & creative assistance), and to Dave Hensel, Mike Sandman, Jason Gardiner, Ron Nash, Paul Thompson, Jason Bickham, Rob Mullins, Roy Fox, Ron Partridge of Panduit, Michael Lizama of Wavetek, Jaquie Smith-Coyote of Leviton Telcom, Jay & Mark Megan of FNS, Lee Richardson of NFPA, and Vernon Menard.

I also want to thank Harry Newton for his contribution of the foreword.

Discounted high volume prices are available for this book for promotional, resale and corporate purchases. Please contact CNC Press for information.

Foreword

Why I Love This Book

By Harry Newton
Author of *Newton's Telecom Dictionary*

29 years in telecom has taught me one thing: It's always the cable. Before you get creative about troubleshooting fancy-schmanzy telecom hardware or software, check your cable. 99% of the time, the problem is in your cable. You skimped. You put the wrong stuff in. You put in too little.

Cables are our lifeblood. They carry our children's voices. They carry the E-mails that make business easier. They tell us what's on at the local movie house. They let us improve our health by checking medical knowledge on the Internet. They let us call the ambulance when we're sick. They bring the fire department.

In all the glamour and excitement of modern communications, the lowly cable and its good (or bad) installation usually get ignored. Yet the dividends of lousy cable and bad installation are many: crackling and hum on conversations, 90% drop in data speed, wasted time on re-sending faxes, total cutoff.

This book won't make you an instant expert on communications cables and their correct installation. Only practice will. But this book will give you a great grounding (pun intended). Follow its clear step-by-step, practical, easy-to-follow instructions, and its great photographs...and bingo you have all the elements of knowing what you need to know about installation and troubleshooting of communications cabling.

Best of all, Jim Abruzzino's excellent handbook makes a great companion to my *Newton's Telecom Dictionary*, which, at 900 pages, makes up in weight what it sadly lacks in practicality.

Introduction

The communications cabling industry continues to explode in size, as it has for years. However, the industry is often plagued by horrible installation practices, spurred by two causes: carelessness, and more commonly, ignorance.

This book was written to provide an easy-to-read, up-to-date guide to communications cabling. It is intended for LAN administrators, cabling technicians, electricians, phone technicians, and anyone else who installs, maintains, or troubleshoots network cabling systems.

Anyone can haphazardly string up network cabling, but installing it correctly very important in order to maintain a reliable network. Long ago, each individual computer system had its own cabling standards that had to be strictly followed for the system to work. Today, there are cabling standards that outline a generic cable infrastructure. Many network systems can be adapted to use this generic infrastructure, and many network systems directly support it.

The Telecommunications Industry Association (TIA) is the creator of the generic cabling infrastructure. The guidelines for large commercial cabling systems are contained in a standards document called TIA/EIA-568-A. You will encounter references to this standard throughout this book. The TIA publishes many other cabling standards, and some information about them is contained in chapter eight.

If you are new to cabling, read through this book in order from start to finish to become familiar with network cabling. If something is unclear to you, do not become frustrated. Simply skip over it, and it is very likely you will come to understand it as you read further.

If you currently install network cabling, then this book will be a valuable reference. Each individual page is labeled so you can quickly find what you are looking for. Use the *hot index* to find the most commonly used pages.

The *Quick Index* is a guide to the most commonly needed pages.

Quick Index

Table of Contents

Chapter 10: Residential/Voice Cabling

Color Codes:

Chapter 1

Identifying Hardware

Introduction

This chapter will help you identify common cables, tools, testers, and equipment. Read this chapter and become familiar with its contents before continuing to later chapters.

New Terms in this Chapter

Conductor

Any material that conducts electricity. In the context of cabling, it means one individual insulated wire. The term *bare conductor* refers to a wire without its insulation.

Termination

A connector at the end of a cable.

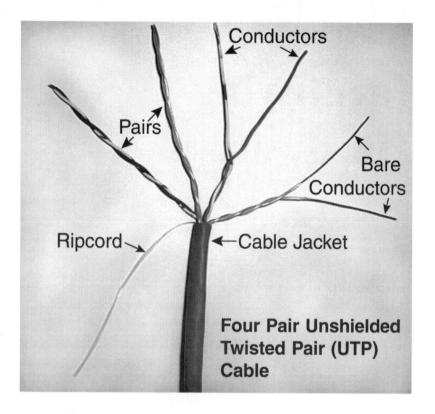

Conductors

Pairs

Bare Conductors

Ripcord

←Cable Jacket

Four Pair Unshielded Twisted Pair (UTP) Cable

Parts of the Four Pair UTP Cable

Two conductors make up a pair. There are four pairs of conductors in this cable, for a total of eight conductors. The cable jacket can also be called a cable sheath. Many manufacturers also include a ripcord, but the ripcord is not very useful in four pair cables.

Unshielded Twisted Pair (UTP)

This is the most popular type of cable. Most of this book concentrates on UTP. It is made up of four pairs of two conductors per pair. The string going upwards is a ripcord.

Screened Twisted Pair (ScTP)

Similar to UTP but has a foil shield between the conductors and the cable jacket. It also has a drain wire (a bare conductor). The drain wire is shown going upwards.

Coaxial

Coaxial cable has one center conductor with a braid and/or foil shield around it.

Shielded Twisted Pair (STP)

Standardized by IBM, this cable is used in many older networks. It has a braid around the cable and a foil shield around each pair. There is also a ripcord on the outside of the foil & braid.

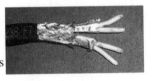

100 Pair UTP

This UTP cable has 100 pairs (200 total conductors) and is used mostly for telephone backbone cabling. Cables are also available in 50, 200, 300, 500 and other pair counts.

Common Termination Methods

UTP Modular Plug

These are used to terminate UTP patch cords. A clip on the plug holds it into the jack.

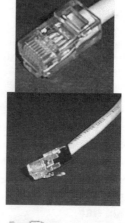

ScTP Modular Plug

These are used to terminate ScTP patch cords. They have metal areas to connect the cable's foil shield with the equipment that it is plugged into.

BNC Connector

These are used to terminate coaxial cable. It has a twist-lock mechanism to hold it on its jack.

F-Type Connector

These are used to terminate coaxial cable. This connector is mostly used for video applications. It screws onto the jack.

UDC Connector

These are used to terminate 2-pair STP cable. When using UDC connectors, keep in mind there is no jack (female end) or plug (male end), both are identical.

110 Cross-Connect

Cross-connects provide an organized way to splice cables. They are also commonly used for connecting 25+ Pair cables to 4 pair cables.

110 Patch Panel

Patch panels are very commonly used as a cross-connect for data networks.

110 Jack

These mount on wall faceplates to provide end users with a port to connect to the network. See chapter 4 for more information.

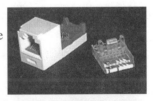

IDC Clip Jack

These mount on wall faceplates to provide end users with a port to connect to the network. See chapter 4 for more information.

66 Cross-Connect

These have similar functions as 110 cross-connects but are mostly used in phone installations.

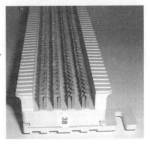

UTP/ScTP Cable Strip Tool

These are several types of strip tools for UTP and ScTP cable.

Punch-down Tool

These are used to punch cables onto cross-connects, patch panels, and jacks. *Punching* a cable means forcing it into an Insulation Displacement Connector (IDC) (for more about IDCs see page 43).

Punch tools come in two varieties: non-impact and impact. Non-impact tools are less costly, and they push a conductor into its connector. Impact punch tools have a spring mechanism that delivers a jolt of force to the conductor being punched, which helps ensure the cable is properly seated. Impact punch tools are advantageous for most applications.

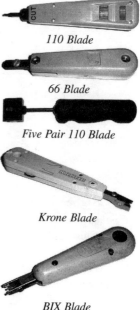

110 Blade

66 Blade

Five Pair 110 Blade

Krone Blade

BIX Blade

Common Tools Used For Cabling

Crimp Tool

Crimp tools form connectors onto cables. They are used for BNC, F-Type, modular and other connectors.

Crimp Die

These are the parts of the crimp tool that actually come in contact with the connector that is being crimped. Crimp dies are interchangeable and many types are available.

Round Cutter

These are used to cut cables with a rounded blade.

Electricians' Scissors

These are used to cut cables with a flat blade.

Fish Tape

This rigid tape is used to pull cable through ceilings and conduit. Fiberglass fish tape is far more expensive than steel but offers the protection of not being conductive.

Modular Breakout Adapter

Allows the technician to access each individual conductor of a cable. Sometimes called a *banjo clip*.

Tone Generator

Puts a tone on the cable that can be picked up with the inductive amplifier. Tone generators are often called *toners*.

Inductive Amplifier

Amplifies inductive signals. These are used with the tone generator to identify cables. These are often called *probes*.

Continuity Tester

Perform basic tests on cables. See chapter 3 for more information.

WaveTek LanTek

Performs advanced tests on cables. See chapter 7 for more information on performance testers.

Scope Comm. WireScope 155

Performs advanced tests on cables. See chapter 7 for more information on performance testers.

Fluke DSP-2000

Performs advanced tests on cables. See chapter 7 for more information on performance testers.

Datacomm LANcat System 6

Performs advanced tests on cables. See chapter 7 for more information on performance testers.

Chapter 2

Twisted Pair Cabling

Introduction

This chapter starts with basic information about four pair UTP and ScTP cabling, then proceeds on to instructions on how to terminate (put an end on) UTP and ScTP cable. You will learn how to crimp on modular plugs, which are at the ends of patch cords.

Some installation companies make their own patch cords so they can carefully control their length. However, many major manufacturers recommend that you do not terminate patch cords in the field, since patch cords made in a manufacturing environment are usually better quality.

New Terms in This Chapter

MHz

Megahertz. One million cycles per second. Relates to the speed in which electrical signals change in the cable.

Strain Relief

The connection that bonds a cable's jacket to a termination so the individual conductors don't have to absorb pulling tension from the cable.

The Construction of UTP Cable

Most UTP cables have eight conductors. These are organized into four pairs. Each pair has a *ring* conductor, and a *tip* conductor. The tip is colored white, and might have colored stripes. The ring is a solid color, but might have white stripes.

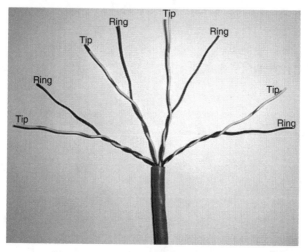

The conductors of each pair are twisted around each other at a constant rate. However, each pair has different twist lengths. These exact lengths vary between manufacturers and types of cable. An example is shown below.

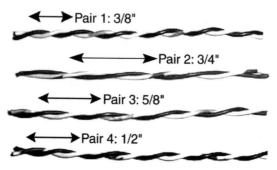

The Strain Relief

When a plug is crimped, either nine or ten individual crimps are made. Eight pins are crimped, one into each of the eight conductors. There are also two *strain reliefs* that either one or both are crimped.

The function of the strain relief is to connect the cable jacket to the plug, so the individual conductor crimps don't have to bear as much of the tension between the cable and the plug.

Secondary Strain Relief   Primary Strain Relief

The primary strain relief crimps onto the cable's outer jacket. The secondary strain relief crimps onto the insulation of each individual conductor. Not all crimp dies crimp the secondary strain relief.

AMP Plugs

AMP brand modular plugs have a nonstandard location of the secondary strain relief. For this reason, they have proprietary crimp dies. Crimping an AMP plug with a standard crimp die will destroy the plug and possibly the die. The same goes for crimping a standard plug with an AMP crimp die. However, a crimp die that crimps only the primary strain relief will work for either type of plug.

Cables are rated by performance. The higher the rating, the less signal degradation happens. Note that only Categories 3, 4, 5 and 5E are recognized by the TIA/EIA-568-A standard (and its revisions).

Name	Speed Rating	Comments
Level 1	N/A	Includes all untwisted cable and much older phone wire. This is only acceptable for voice or very low speed data.
Level 2	1 MHz	Obsolete for new data installations. Includes IBM STP cabling.
Category 3	16 MHz	Commonly used for phone installations, most current local area networks can use this cable. Not recommended for new data installations.
Category 4	20 MHz	This is not commonly seen, since its subtle improvement over category 3 was quickly overshadowed by category 5.
Category 5	100 MHz	Minimum recommended for all new data and voice installations.
Category 5E	100 MHz	Costs near the same as Category 5, and provides better performance characteristics. Standardized by TIA/EIA-568-A-5
Category 6	250 MHz (Expected)	This has not yet been standardized, but many manufacturers are making Category 6 cable based on expectations of what the standard will say.

Future Cable Ratings

The cabling industry expects standards for Category 6 and 7 in the coming years. There is no certainty at this time about what changes will occur in the cabling industry as a result of new standards. Read trade magazines for updated information.

Types of Conductors

Conductor Size

The conductors in most UTP and ScTP cables are 24 gauge copper wire. Some manufacturers use other sizes of wire. As long as the cable is marked with the category rating you want, its conductor size is not a concern.

Conductor Type

Cables can have solid or stranded conductors. Stranded conductors are more flexible because they consist of many thin strands of wire twisted together. Solid conductors have one solid copper wire as a conductor. Solid cable is less expensive than stranded. Article 10.5.3 of the TIA/EIA-568-A standard specifies that patch cords are to be made out of stranded cable.

When specifying modular plugs, be careful to match them to the conductor type. Modular plugs made for stranded conductors will not crimp properly if used on solid conductors. Modular plugs made for solid conductors usually work for stranded cable, but check your manufacturer's suggestions.

These problems are due to the way the Insulation Displacement Connectors (IDC) in the plug pierce the cable, as illustrated below.

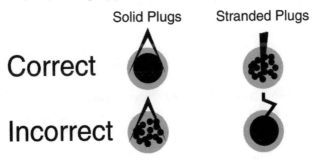

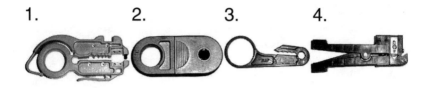

1. 2. 3. 4.

First...

Tool 1

Squeeze the round end to open the tool and slide your cable to the proper strip position. In most cases, you will use the biggest strip position.

Tool 2

Put your middle finger through the big loop and push the plastic grip edge with your thumb and forefinger. Insert the cable into the small hole.

Tool 3

Slide your cable to the proper strip position. In most cases, you will use the biggest strip position.

Tool 4

Squeeze the tool like a clothespin and insert the cable into the groove.

Then...

Rotate the tool once around the cable and remove the tool. Do not pull the tool to the end of the cable to remove the jacket, doing so destroys the cutting blade. Some cable brands may need different stripping procedures, so practice on a scrap piece if necessary. Rotating the strip tool too many times around the cable will damage the individual conductors' insulation.

Bend the cable back and forth to break off the jacket and remove the broken piece. Remember that the strip tool is not meant to cut the jacket off, it is only supposed to score the jacket so it will break off easily.

Terminating UTP to Modular Plugs

What You Will Make

You are about to make a UTP patch cord. Patch cords are a point to point connection between equipment and modular jacks or patch panels. Patch cords are rarely more than 20 feet long and they are not supposed to run between rooms.

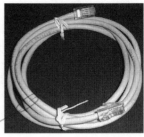

patch cord

Step 1

Strip off one inch of the cable jacket using instructions on page 26. Untwist the conductors to the edge of the cable jacket. Cut off the ripcord (if one exists).

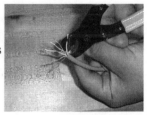

Step 2

Arrange the conductors into the pattern you desire. Look on page 186 for color code reference.

Step 3

Trim the edges of the conductors straight, about one half inch from the jacket. The maximum untwisted conductor length for Category 5 is 1/2". The end of the conductors **must** be trimmed straight or else they will not enter the plug completely.

* For notes about using solid conductor cable with a plug, see page 25.
* If you are using AMP plugs or crimp dies, see page 23.

Terminating UTP to Modular Plugs

Step 4

Carefully slip the plug onto the cable. Be careful to keep the conductors in their proper order as they enter the connector. There are two easy ways to make sure the plug is facing the right way when inserting cables: 1. Like a boat, the rudder (the clip) is down, 2. There is a window to see the conductors on top.

Step 5

Look through the top of the plug and make sure all of the conductors are in their correct places. The conductors should be in the same order as they are in their diagram on page 186.

Step 6

Before crimping, look at the side of the plug. The cable jacket should extend past the primary strain relief in the plug. Also, look at the front end of the plug. You should see the shiny ends of each conductor, showing you that the conductors are seated all the way in the plug.

Step 7

While making you don't pull the cable out of the plug, put the plug into the crimp tool. Squeeze the crimp tool completely, usually it will click when completely engaged. Release the handle and remove your plug from the tool.

Step 8

Don't forget to always test all cables.

Using ScTP Cable

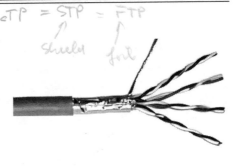

(handwritten: ScTP = STP = FTP, shield, foil)

ScTP stands for *Screened Twisted Pair*. It is also sometimes called Shielded Twisted Pair (STP), but the term "STP" should be reserved for the 2 pair STP you will work with in chapter 5 (or cable that has a foil shield around *each pair*).

ScTP cable has a foil shield surrounding all four pairs. There is also an bare drain wire that is used for terminating the shield.

ScTP is also sometimes called FTP (Foiled Twisted Pair), but this term is not very common.

When using ScTP cable, make sure the connecting equipment has provisions for grounding the shield. The TIA/EIA-607 standard explains proper *grounding & bonding*. Grounding is establishing an electrically continuous path to the ground, while bonding is making permanent ground connections using screws & lugs.

What You Will Make

You are about to make an ScTP patch cable. ScTP cables perform the same function as UTP patch cables, but the cable has an outside foil shield and the plugs connect the shield to the equipment.

Step 1

Remember to rotate the strip tool only 360 degrees once to avoid cutting the foil shield. Remove the strip tool, and bend the cable back and forth to break the jacket, and remove the jacket. At this point the shield should be left intact on the cable. If the foil is sliced, cut off the end and try to strip the cable again. It might take you a couple tries.

Step 2

Carefully peel the foil and fold it back. Be careful not to rip the foil. Fold back the drain wire.

Step 3

Separate the plastic wrapping, if one exists, from the pairs and cut it off. Failure to remove the plastic can result in loss of shield continuity since plastic is an insulator.

Step 4

Arrange the conductors using the configuration of your choice. If you are unclear on color codes, refer to page 186. If you are using AMP brand plugs, there will be a black clip to hold the conductors in place, as shown.

Step 5

Trim the edges of the conductors straight, about one half inch from the jacket. Carefully hold the plug and slip the conductors into the plug. Remember the analogy that, like a boat, the plug keeps its "rudder side down."

Step 6

Verify that all of the conductors are in their proper places. Look at the end of the plug, and you should see all eight ends of conductors to verify that all of the conductors have entered the plug properly. Also check that the cable jacket is under the strain relief tab.

Step 7

While making sure the conductors remain seated in the plug, put the plug into the crimp tool. Squeeze the crimp tool completely, usually it will click when completely engaged. Release the handle and remove your plug from the tool. You may trim the foil back a little bit to make it look neater. Don't forget to test the cable.

* If you are using AMP brand plugs or crimp dies, refer to page 23.

Chapter 3
Testing Cable

Introduction

Cabling must always be tested after it has been terminated, installed, moved or changed. This may be as simple as a test to verify all conductors are connected correctly (a *continuity, wiremap or pin-out* test), or can be as thorough as a test that puts high-speed data over the cable (a *performance* test). Most technicians only carry with them a continuity tester, since performance testers are significantly more expensive.

New Terms in this Chapter
Continuity

A path of low resistance for current flow from one point to another point.

Open Conductor

There is a lack of continuity in any of the conductors between the two ends of a cable run.

Miswire

A conductor is not in its correct place at either end.

Reversed Pair

The tip and ring conductors of a pair are reversed with each other.

Transposed Pair

Two pairs are in each others' places, tip-tip and ring-ring. For example, a cable with a plug in the T568A pattern on one end and the T568B pattern on the other end has transposed pairs two and three.

Short

There is unwanted continuity between two conductors or between a conductor and the shield.

Split Pair

The cable may have pin-by-pin continuity, but the pairs are not matched correctly in order for the signals to be balanced.

Illustrations for the above are on pages 190-191.

Ideal PathFinder

The Ideal PathFinder tests UTP, ScTP and coaxial cables. It uses flashing indicator LEDs to show cable problems.

Paladin Patch-Check Plus

The Patch-Check Plus tests the cable by each pin, rather than by the pair like the STM-8 and PathFinder.

Siemon STM-8

The Siemon STM-8 tests continuity and performs a basic transmission test to detect split pairs. The standard STM-8 only tests UTP cable, and the ScTP version of the tester (with active remote) tests ScTP and UTP.

Fluke CableMeter 620

The Fluke CableMeter 620 performs all of the basic continuity tests, but also has the ability to also indicate the distance to the fault. It also displays cable length.

Introduction to the Siemon STM-8

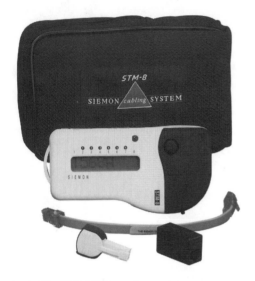

The Siemon STM-8 is a wiremap tester. It is one of the most commonly used testers in the cabling industry.

The STM-8 is used with a remote unit. The remote must be plugged into the opposite end of the cable being tested.

Newly re-designed STM-8 Remote

The STM-8 is made to withstand telephone line voltages without tester damage. If the unit ever displays the message LINE VOLTAGE, disconnect it immediately.

If the STM-8 displays TOO SHRT while testing, the cable being tested is too short to be tested with the transmission test. The cable must be at least three feet long for the STM-8 to perform this test. If this is displayed, the cable may still be wired correctly, but it is not long enough to run the test on.

The photographs on this page are courtesy of The Siemon Company.

Capabilities of the STM-8

Push the black button to turn on the STM-8. Keep pushing the button until correct option (T568A, etc.) is selected. The cable is tested as soon as you release the button for about two seconds. The following options are available:

T568A
Tests cable in the T568A configuration.

SCTP568A
Tests screened cable in the T568A configuration, and tests the shield.

T568B
Tests cable in the T568B configuration.

SCTP568B
Tests screened cable in the T568B configuration, and tests the shield.

USOC
Tests cable in the USOC configuration.

10BASE-T
Tests only the pins used for 10Base-T networks: pins 1,2,3, and 6 (2 pairs).

TOK-RING
Tests only the pins used for Token Ring networks: pins 3,4,5, and 6 (2 pairs).

TP-PMD
Tests only the pins used for Twisted Pair-Physical Medium Dependent (TP-PMD) networks: pins 1,2,7, and 8 (2 pairs).

FIND
Finds the wiring pattern: T568 (either A or B), USOC, 10Base-T, Token Ring, or TP-PMD.

TONE MOD
Generates a tone on the cable for an inductive probe to find. After waiting for a couple seconds, push the button again to select which pin to put the tone on.

TALK BAT
Puts electrical current on the line to power two phones to communicate with each other.

T568B

The T568B configuration is selected.

Remote A

Each remote has a letter printed on it for cable identification.

CC

Tests pairs 1,2,3, and 4 in T568B configuration for continuity. This is a basic wiremap test. Below is a table of cable condition codes:

CC	Passes Continuity	TT	Passes Transmission Test
XX	Miswire	OO	Open
RR	Reversal	??	Unknown or Multiple Errors
SS	Short		

TT

Checks whether the pairs are connected correctly. The test will fail if there is a split pair (explained on page 191).

Pass

(or fail) Indicates whether the cable passed all tests.

The grids below have 8 boxes across to represent the STM-8 display. The rows each show the STM-8's display as the test progresses.

T568A Pass   T568B Pass   USOC Pass   10B/T Pass   T. Ring Pass   TP-PMD Pass

Using the Ideal PathFinder

The PathFinder tests for continuity faults in a cable. It will check for opens, shorts, reversed pairs, split pairs, and transposed pairs. The PathFinder also has a tone generator.

The PathFinder requires a remote to be plugged into the opposite end of the cable being tested. The remotes can also help you identify cables. The four remotes are labeled A, B, C, and D. The PathFinder flashes lights to show which remote is plugged in.

To test for split pairs, there must be at least six feet of cable between the PathFinder and remote. If the cable is shorter, a red light will blink even though the cable might be OK. Ideal recommends using the *Ideal Wiring Verifier* for testing patch cords.

To use the PathFinder, press *test/select*. It will perform a basic cable test using the last configuration you set it to. To change the test configuration, press *mode* until the CONFIG LED is lit. Press the *test/select* button until the configuration you want to test with is selected. Push the *mode* button again.

The PathFinder also has a learn mode. Using this, the PathFinder tests a known good cable, then can test other cables based on the results of the learned test. This is useful when you test installations that are not made to standards or common wiring patterns.

Chapter 4

Horizontal & Backbone Cabling

Introduction

Horizontal cabling is considered permanent cabling. It is installed in walls and ceilings and is secured in place. It does not normally pass between floors of a building. The basic horizontal link is between a work area outlet (WAO) and a patch panel. Backbone cabling connects telecom closets and/or equipment rooms, and often passes between floors of a building. Four pair UTP can be used for backbone or horizontal cabling, but 25+ pair cables are used only for backbone cabling.

A cross-connect is hardware that connects two cables together. A patch panel is a type of cross-connect. However, in the context of cabling hardware, from here and on 110 patch panels will be spoken of separately than 110 cross-connects for clarity.

New Terms in this Chapter
Link

A point to point connection. For instance, the horizontal link is between the work area outlet and the patch panel. Compare with channel.
Channel

(Also *Station Run*) The complete cable run from hub to the equipment or computer. This includes the patch cords, horizontal cabling, cross-connects, and jacks.

Types of Connections

Wire Wrap and Solder

Long ago, soldering and wire wrap dominated cable connections.
Both of these required a long time to install or change. Many old buildings
still have large boards of wire wrapped or soldered connections. Although
wire wrap is still used in many telephone company related applications,
solder for cross-connects is obsolete.

Screw Post

Screw posts are still used on many residential
jacks. To install a conductor to a screw binding
post, strip the conductor back about 1/2 inch and
unscrew the post. Insert the bare conductor *between*
the two washers to prevent the screw from breaking
the cable. Wrap the cable around the post and avoid
having loose ends of bare copper stick out of the
washer. Tighten the post, but do not make it so tight as to strip the screw's
threads.

Insulation Displacement Connector (IDC)

The Insulation Displacement Connector (IDC) has replaced all of the
above methods as the ideal termination in new installations. The IDC
pierces the cable jacket and makes a connection with the conductor. There
is no need for the installer to strip off the conductor's insulation. Since
IDCs are very small, they can be placed very close together to reduce the
size of cross-connects. IDCs are the best termination for high speed data
cabling since a gas-tight, uniform connection is made.

IDCs come in many forms. 66, 110, BIX, and Krone cross-connects
are based on this connector. The modular plugs you installed in chapter 2
use IDCs. IDC clip jacks also use IDC connectors.

IDC Connector Types

Each type of IDC connector on this page requires its unique type of punchdown die.

110 Connector

These are the most popular connectors for new installations. 110 Patch panels are typically rated Category 5, but always check a cross-connect or patch panel's rating before ordering them.

Krone

Krone cross-connects have a patented 45 degree angled IDC, which surpasses standard 110 connectors in its transmission properties.

BIX

BIX is made by NORDX/CDT. BIX IDCs have superior transmission properties to 110 connectors.

66 Clip

66 blocks are typically rated Category 3, and are used mostly for voice applications. Category 5 66 blocks are available.

IDC Clip

IDC Clip is the newest method of jack termination. They are typically more costly than 110 but some people find them easier to install.

Using 110-Type Cross-Connects

110-type cross-connects are used in all types of applications, but they are most commonly used for telephone cabling. Their function is to simply connect two conductors; they splice hundreds of conductors, neatly, and in a small area. The bottom block only holds the cable in place, the actual IDC is in the connector block. After cables are punched down on the bottom block (bottom picture), connector blocks are installed on top of them.

There are two common ways to use this type of cross-connect:

1. The horizontal (or backbone) four pair cabling is punched down on the cross-connect block. Four pair connector blocks are then inserted down on top of where the cable is first punched down. Four pair patch cords are punched down, or 110 adapters are placed on top of the connector blocks.

2. 25 pair (or a multiple of 25) cable is punched down on the bottom of the cross-connect block. Four pair patch cables or horizontal runs are punched down on top of the connector blocks. This setup is common where voice backbone cabling connects with horizontal cabling.

Connector Blocks

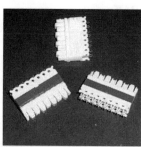

110 Cross-Connect Block

Using 110-Type Cross-Connects

In the picture below, the middle cable ID strip has been removed. The incoming cables (on the bottom half of the block) are covered up by the cable ID strip. Although it is a very commonly broken rule in phone installations, the cable jacket should be maintained as close as possible to the termination point.

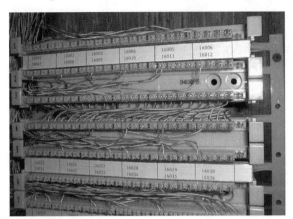

Orange Brown
Blue | Green /

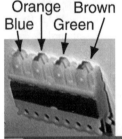

The illustration at the bottom shows the positions for four pair cables on 110-type cross-connects. The left illustration shows placement for four pairs on the connector block. There are also colored dots on the connector block that show where pairs are to be punched down. The tip conductor of the pair goes on the left side and the ring on the right.

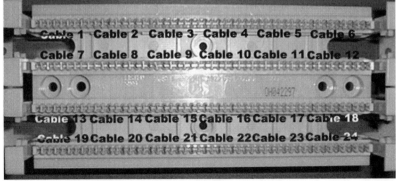

Cable 1 Cable 2 Cable 3 Cable 4 Cable 5 Cable 6
Cable 7 Cable 8 Cable 9 Cable 10 Cable 11 Cable 12
Cable 13 Cable 14 Cable 15 Cable 16 Cable 17 Cable 18
Cable 19 Cable 20 Cable 21 Cable 22 Cable 23 Cable 24

Using 110-Type Cross-Connects

Even though this type of cross-connect was originally designed for 25 pair or larger cables, they are also commonly used with four pair cables. The color codes printed on these blocks are for 25 pair cables.

After the bottom layer of cables on the block have been punched down, connector blocks are installed on top of the punched down cables. Cable ID strips are installed on top of the bottom layer of cables to hide the bottom layer of cables and mark the cable or port numbers of the top layer of cables. Since these blocks have 25 pair spaces per row, there will be an empty pair space (2 conductors) at the end if four pair cables are used. This can either be left empty or a five pair connector block can be installed in the rightmost position.

There is no simple rule for terminating four pair ScTP cables on these blocks. One way is to use every fifth pair position to terminate the shield. Punch a short jumper between the ring and tip on the bottom of the block. After a 5-pair connector block is installed, punch the drain wire from the incoming cable into the tip position of pair 5, and a conductor from the ring to the TGB (Telecommunications Grounding Busbar). Note: Use of the grounding busbar is covered in the NEC section 800-40 and the TIA/EIA-607 standard.

In the voice system example to the left, the 25 pair backbone comes in on the bottom layer of the left block, and jumper cables (over the top) connect that block to the outgoing four pair cables on the right side. All four pairs are punched down on the bottom of the right block, but only pair one is connected (with a jumper wire) to the backbone. Many voice systems are interconnected in this way. Make sure you only strip off as much cable jacket as necessary.

Using 66 Cross-Connects

Like 110 cross-connect blocks, 66 blocks are sometimes used to splice 25 pair backbone cables to horizontal runs. For this reason, the most common 66-type blocks are 25 pair spaces long. When punching down four pair cables, the order is as shown at left. Since there are no color or cable codes printed on the actual blocks, you need to be careful when making terminations.

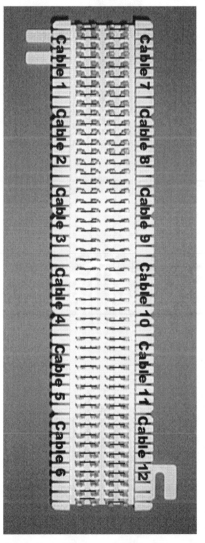

66 Blocks can be purchased in many configurations. They come in four (66m) or six (66b) conductors wide. The most common internal connection scheme is shown to the left with black lines. These blocks can also be purchased with an internal connection between all four or six clips across.

The tip conductor is punched down on the left side of its matching ring conductor. Since these blocks are commonly mounted vertically, the tip will be on top and the ring below. The pair order is: 1, 2, 3, 4; next cable: 1, 2, 3, 4; repeating.

Since the 66 block was designed for 25-pair cables, one pair position will be vacant at the end of each row when four pair cables are punched down.

The block at the left is marked with the positions for four pair cables and the black lines show the 66M-150 block's internal connections.

Terminating 110 Style Jacks

Step 1

Strip the cable back about 2" and spread out the pairs.

Step 2

Look at the side of the jack. There should be color codes that tell you where cables are to be terminated on the jack. A half-solid dot with white stripe represents tip and a solid dot represents ring. The color codes might be on top of the 110 block. Be sure to verify whether the jack is wired for T568A, T568B, or USOC.

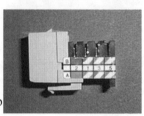

Step 3

Put the cable jacket up to the back edge of the jack. Bend the pairs so they roughly align to their positions.

Step 4

Seat the conductors according to the color codes printed on the sides of the jack. If there are dots on top of the 110 block, then the tip goes on the left of the dot and the ring on the right.

Communications Cabling

Step 5

Take the punchdown tool and punch down
the conductors. Make sure the cutting blade on
the tool is pointed outwards so you do not cut
the conductor before it enters the 110 block.

Step 6

Inspect your termination. If there is a
problem, pull the whole cable off and re-
terminate. Do not pull up a single connector and
punch it down again as doing so will often cause
a faulty connection. Install the caps that were
provided with the jack over the 110 connectors.

Terminating IDC Clip Jacks

Step 1

Strip off about one inch of cable jacket. Untwist the pairs to the edge of the jacket.

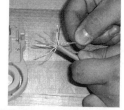

Step 2

Arrange the conductors according the color code printed on the termination cap. Trimming the conductors at an angle will make them easier to insert into the termination cap. Slide the termination cap onto the conductors.

Step 3

Make sure there is one conductor per groove and the conductors are straight over the openings (as shown).

Step 4

Trim off the excess wire as shown. After trimming, inspect the cap to ensure all conductors are in their correct positions. Also make sure that the pairs are not untwisted more than 1/2" in order to comply with Category 5 specifications.

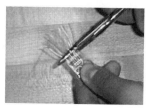

Step 5

Align the termination cap with the groove on the jack.

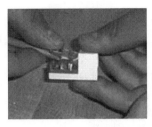

Step 6

Press the termination cap onto the jack until it clicks in place. You might need to use slip joint pliers, or some companies provide a special thumb lever. Inspect the wires carefully to ensure all of them are in place.

Re-Termination

If the conductors are not positioned correctly, or there is another problem with the termination, carefully unlatch both sides of the termination cap with the flat-head screwdriver and lift. Cut off the untwisted conductors and start over.

Terminating Cross-Connect Blocks

Step 1

Remove 2-3" of the cable jacket and cut off the ripcord.

Step 2

Use the chart on page 45 to find the position for your cable. Separate the pairs and roughly position then over their positions.

Step 3

Untwist a pair one time to leave a loop that you can use to seat the conductors. Remember that the ring goes on the right side of the color dot and the tip goes on the left. Ignore the color of the dot, since these blocks are usually marked for 25 pair cables. Depending on what is comfortable for you, you can punch down each conductor as you seat them, or you can punch them all once they are all in place.

Step 4

Use the punchdown tool to punch each conductor into place. Make sure the cutting blade on the punchdown tool is positioned outwards so it will not cut the cable you are punching down.

Communications Cabling

Step 6

Position a connector block over the pairs that are already punched down. Line up the colors so the color dots on the top of the connector will be straight over the pair of that color. **Note:** Often, installers will punch down the entire bottom layer of the 110 base before installing connector blocks.

Step 7

Position the punch tool in one of the middle positions of the connector block. Push down hard to seat the connector block. It may require pounding with your hand or use of an impact punch tool.

Step 8

Untwist a loop as you did in step 3. The connector block will have the color codes on the center posts, so all you have to do is seat the ring of the color to the right and the tip to the left. After all of the pairs are seated, punch them down.

Inspect your termination to ensure that no more than 1/2" of pair untwist is present. Also, contrary to what was practiced in the past with phone cross-connects, article 10.6.3.2 of the TIA/EIA-568-A standard dictates that the cable jacket should be maintained as close to the termination point as possible.

Terminating 110 Patch Panels

Step 1

Strip off 2-3" of cable jacket. Cut off the ripcord. Arrange the pairs from left to right: 1,2,3,4.

Step 2

Find the position for your cable. There is usually a paper strip labeling the port numbers for each 110 connector. In this case we are using port 14. When installing a whole block, start from the outside and work your way into the middle to avoid *burying* a port by putting cables over it.

Step 3

Untwist one twist of pair 1 close to the edge of the cable jacket.

Step 4

Locate the post with the color dot for the pair. Slide the loop down onto either side of the post, with the ring on the right and the tip on the left. Repeat this for all four pairs.

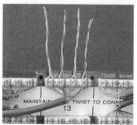

Step 5

Punch down each conductor with the punch down tool. Make sure the cutting blade is pointed in the correct direction. Avoid using a four pair punchdown tool on printed circuit board (PCB) based patch panels, since the high impact of the tool can damage the PCB.

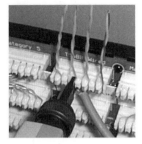

Step 6

Inspect your termination. No pair should be untwisted more than one half inch. The cable jacket should be maintained as close to the termination as possible.

Terminating 66 Cross-Connects

Step 1

Strip off about two inches of cable jacket.
Cut off the ripcord.

Step 2

Refer to page 47 for a reference on 4-pair
punchdown positions for 66-type cross-connects.

Step 3

The pair must still be twisted as it passes
through one of the white channels. Push one
pair through every other channel. Pull them all
through until the cable jacket is against the side
of the block, but not tight enough to put
backwards tension on the pairs.

Step 4

Untwist each pair after it passes through
the white channels.

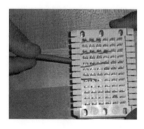

Step 5

Insert each conductor onto its clip in the block. Remember the order from right to left, or top to bottom is pair 1 tip, 1 ring, 2 tip, 2 ring, 3 tip, 3 ring, 4 tip, 4 ring.

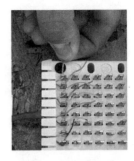

Step 6

Use the punchdown tool and punch down each conductor. Make sure the cutting blade is on the correct side, and make sure you are not cutting other conductors on adjacent clips.

Removing Conductors

Many technicians use a *spudger* to remove conductors from 66 blocks. The one shown here is on a punch tool, however, they can also be purchased separately.

Chapter 5

Coaxial and 2 Pair STP Cable

Introduction

Coaxial cable distribution requires fewer termination types than twisted pair cabling. Unlike twisted pair cabling, work area outlets and patch panels for coaxial cabling typically have the same type of connector on both sides of the panel or faceplate. For example, in cable TV distribution, you might have an F-type connector to F-type connector patch cable between the wall and the TV. On the other side of the faceplate, you will have a F-type to F-type horizontal cable to the cable TV distribution panel or splitter.

New Terms in this Chapter

CCTV

Closed Circuit Television- A video distribution system that does not leave the building or campus.

CATV

Community Antenna Television- Also known as *cable television*.

IBM

International Business Machines- A company that makes mainframe computers and has specific cabling specifications for them.

Coaxial Cable Types

Coaxial cable has four major components. There is a solid copper center conductor, a nonconductive dielectric layer, a braid and/or foil shield, and an outer jacket.

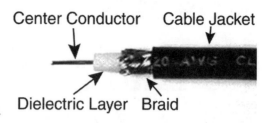

Center Conductor   **Cable Jacket**

Dielectric Layer   **Braid**

There are several factors that determine a coaxial cable's performance. Some are the size of the center conductor, the percentage of shield coverage, materials used in making the cable, and the cable's impedance. To make it easier to specify types of cable, standard cable types are made. Explanations of the cable types are below.

Terminating coaxial cables is relatively easy compared to 4 pair UTP, but there are still several ways to go wrong. Make sure the braid does not short out to the center conductor. Also follow directions carefully when you crimp on the crimp sleeve, since the connector can be easily pulled off if the crimp sleeve is not properly installed. Always tug on coaxial connectors after installing them to make sure they will not come off.

The following are popular types of coaxial cable:

Type	Nominal Impedance	Common Uses
RG-6	75 OHM	CATV, CCTV, some older computer networks.
RG-8	50 OHM	Thick Ethernet (10Base-5) Networks
RG-58	50 OHM	Thin Ethernet (10Base-2) Networks
RG-59	75 OHM	CATV, CCTV, Older networks such as broadband Ethernet and ARCnet.
RG-62	93 OHM	Older Computer Networks, IBM 3270.

Communications Cabling

2 Pair STP Cable Types

These are the commonly used types of 2 Pair STP cable:

Type	Pairs	Wire Gauge	Wire Type	Notes
Type 1	2	22	Solid	
Type 2	2	22	Solid	Has four additional 24 gauge UTP pairs for voice
Type 6	2	26	Stranded	Used for short-run patch cords.
Type 9	2	26	Solid	Plenum rated jacket

High Speed STP Rating

The original 150 ohm STP was rated to 20 MHz and is used for token ring networks at up to 16 Mbps. Modern STP components and cable are rated to 300 MHz transmission rate and have a suffix of "A" on the type number (i.e. Type 9a) and/or have *Extended* printed on the jacket. Converter BALUNs (a type of adapter) can adapt this extended cable to handle certain Asynchronous Transfer Mode (ATM) technologies.

Terminating UDC Connectors

Note: These installation instructions are for Thomas & Betts style UDC connectors. The line diagrams are provided courtesy of Thomas & Betts.

Step 1

Strip the cable jacket 1 inch. Place the washer at the end of the cable jacket.

Step 2

Fan out the braid from past the washer and fold it back over the washer. Try to make the braid evenly spread over the washer. Cut off all foil, wrapping, and filler material from past the washer.

Step 3

Spread out the conductors evenly in a fork pattern as shown. Trim conductors to 5/8".

Step 4

Insert conductors into the matching color-coded slots of dressing block, as shown. Make sure that the edges of wires are flush with the end of the wire channels in the dressing block. Press the wires down into their grooves.

Step 5

Make sure the wires are correctly seated in the dressing block.

CORRECT   INCORRECT

Terminating UDC Connectors

Step 6

Align the dressing block with the contact housing, and press the dressing block onto the contacts. Use slip joint pliers to seat the dressing block. Verify that the top of the keys (on the sides on the dressing block) are flush with the top of the groove in the contact housing.

Step 7

Prepare the connector housing by removing one of the rear tabs. Remove the tab pointing in the direction you want the cable to exit through.

Step 8

Place the dressing block into the connector housing. Make sure the washer is in front of the metal divider in the housing. Route the cable through the tab you removed. Trim the braid if it is so long that it sticks out the back.

CORRECT   INCORRECT

Step 10

Align the top cover over the housing and press it on. Six clips will snap in place when the top is correctly seated.

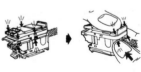

Terminating F-Type Connectors

Step 1

Slide the crimp sleeve onto the cable, and slide it back and out of the way. Strip off 3/8" of the cable jacket using hole A. Unlike while stripping UTP, you must rotate the tool several times around the cable. Its important that the small tension arm on the strip tool is in its groove.

Step 2

Remove the cut insulation and braid. You should be left with a cable similar to that at right.

Step 3

Strip off another 1/4" from the edge of the cable jacket, using hole B on the strip tool. Remove the cut part and use the electrician's scissors to cut off any remaining braid outside of the cable jacket.

Step 4

Insert the center conductor through the middle of the connector. Push the back of the connector into the coaxial cable jacket. It will take force, but wiggling might make it easier. The center conductor should extend 3/16" past the end of the connector shell, cut it back if necessary.

Terminating F-Type Connectors

Step 5

Slide up the crimp sleeve to the back edge of the connector.

Step 6

Crimp the connector in the appropriate crimp position of the crimp tool.

Step 7

Give the connector a sharp tug to make sure it is strongly bonded to the cable. After all, it is better for it to come apart in your hands than the end user's.

Terminating BNC Connectors

Step 1

Insert the crimp sleeve onto the cable and slide it a couple inches down the cable. Strip off 1/4" of outer cable jacket using hole A on the strip tool. Note the distance between the cutting blade and the edge of the tool is approximately 1/4 inch.

Step 2

Remove the cut insulation and braid. The cable will look similar to that at right.

Step 3

Strip off the next 1/4" using hole B on the strip tool. Remove the cut insulation and the cable should look similar to that at right.

Step 4

Strip off the next 1/4" using hole C on the strip tool. Remove the cut insulation and the cable should look similar to that at right.

Step 5

Bend the braid upward like shown at right.

Terminating BNC Connectors

Step 6

Insert the crimp pin onto the center conductor. Hold it in place and carefully crimp the pin using the smallest hole on the crimp tool.

Step 7

Put the crimp pin into the back of the BNC connector and insert it until the back of the BNC connector is flush against the edge of the cable jacket. The center pin should be flush with the top of the BNC connector.

Step 8

Fold the braid back down over the back of the BNC connector. Slide the crimp sleeve up the back of the connector.

Step 9

Check to make sure the center crimp pin is nearly flush with the end of the connector. Then, while holding the connector onto the cable, crimp the sleeve using the appropriate hole on the crimp tool.

Step 10

Give the connector a sharp tug to make sure it is correctly bonded to the cable. Don't forget to test the cable.

Chapter 6
Network Systems

Introduction

It is important not only for the installer to be able to terminate cables, but also to install the cable properly. Much of the rest of this book focuses on installing cable.

The overall layout of the cabling system is known as its topology. Identifying a network's topology is essential to properly installing cable. The topology dictates exactly how cable is run, whether it is between offices, from offices to a central cabling closet, or other methods.

New Terms in this Chapter

Topology

A physical layout.

Packet

A grouping of data signals sent across the network.

Fault Tolerance

The ability for a networking system to keep functioning when cabling or equipment breaks.

LAN Topologies

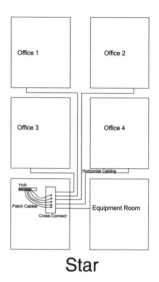

Star

The LAN topology is the physical layout of the network. These are basic diagrams of LAN topologies.

The star topology is the most popular, and it is specified by major cabling standards. Most networks today are made in the star topology.

The daisy chain, ring and linear bus topologies are not recommended for new installations. Many older networks still run on these, and their cabling is and will be significantly harder to maintain.

Note that the ring topology is simply the daisy chain topology with an extra link between the two ends.

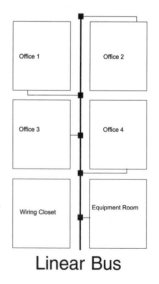

Linear Bus

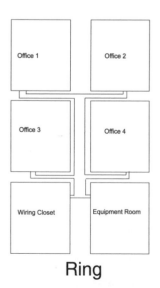

Ring

Communications Cabling

Comparison of LAN Topologies

Star Topology

Advantages	Disadvantages
Ease of additions and changes.	More cable is used.
Very good fault tolerance on cable runs.	Bad fault tolerance if the hub fails.
Compliant with the TIA/EIA-568-A standard.	
Used by most modern network systems, has wide industry support.	

Linear Bus Topology

Ease of adding stations if they are near the backbone cable.	Very poor fault tolerance.
Ideal for long, narrow hallways.	Difficulty of troubleshooting cable problems.
	Difficulty of adding stations if they are far from the backbone.

Ring/Daisy Chain Topology

Ideal for computer rooms/computer labs.	Poor fault tolerance.
	Difficulty of additions, changes and troubleshooting
	Difficulty of running cable between offices.

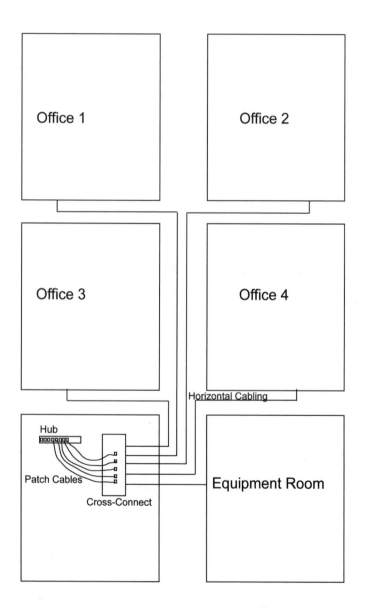

10Base-T & 100Base-T Ethernet

100 Ohm 4 Pair Unshielded Twisted Pair Cabling

Maximum distance from hub to equipment: 100 Meters, without repeaters

10Base-T minimum cabling specification: Category 3, in the star topology.
100Base-T minimum cabling specification: Category 5, in the star topology.

The specifications for Ethernet are contained in IEEE 802.3. Following the TIA/EIA-568-A standard is ideal for this networking system.

Twisted pair Ethernet connects with eight pin modular jacks and plugs. Four pair UTP cable is usually installed, but only two pairs are used, a transmit and a receive line.

Repeaters are devices that regenerate the network signal, to extend the maximum distance of the network. The hub contains a repeater (they can be called a "Multi-port Repeater").

Networks running 10 Mbps Ethernet can be connected to ones running 100 Mbps Ethernet through a 10/100 switch. Switches also split segments. See page 82 for more on switches.

On June 26, 1999, the IEEE ratified 802.3ab, which defines 1000BASE-T as *gigabit ethernet* running over category five cable. Existing Category 5 installations should be tested to comply with TSB-95 before running gigabit ethernet.

10Base-5 Ethernet (Thick Coax)

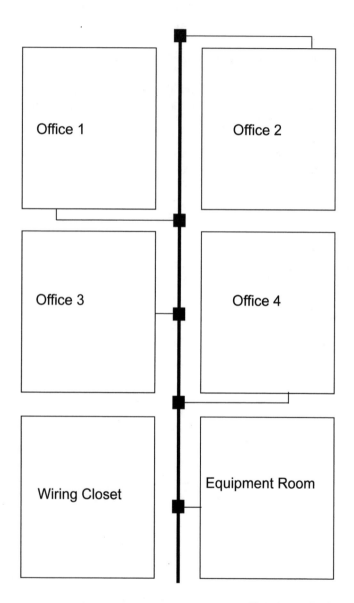

Communications Cabling

10Base-5 Ethernet (Thick Coax)

RG-8 Coaxial Cable
Maximum Distance Per Run: 500 Meters (1640 Feet)
Minimum Distance Between Taps: 2.5 Meters (8 Feet)

Thick coaxial cable in a linear bus topology used to be very popular for Ethernet networks.

It is no longer installed commonly due to the following shortcomings of this setup:
- ⊗ Very rigid cable is hard to install.
- ⊗ Low fault tolerance.

The thick coaxial cable is pierced without being spliced by means of a tap, also commonly known as *Vampire Tap* or *AMP Tap*. The tap then is connected to a transceiver and then to a pre-made patch cord connecting it to the computer.

The maximum users per segment is limited to 100. Their taps must be connected at least eight feet apart. Some thick coaxial cable is marked every eight feet to represent a possible connection point.

Vampire Tap with Transceiver

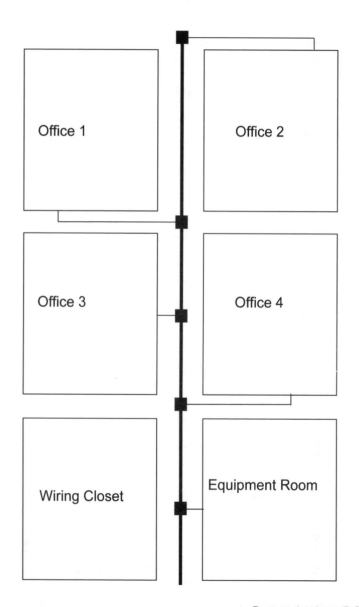

10Base-2 Ethernet (Thin Coax)

RG-58 Coaxial Cable
Maximum Distance Per Run: 607 Feet (185 Meters)
Longest Cable Segment Between Stations: 300 Feet
Minimum Distance Between T-Connectors: 1.5 Feet

When looking at the thin coax network from far away, it looks like it is cabled in the daisy chain topology. However, the way the cables connect to equipment classifies it as linear bus topology.

T-connectors connect two ends of BNC connectorized cables with a BNC connector on the equipment. The end of each cable length has a terminator in place of another cable. The terminator is a small connector that has a resistor between the center conductor and the braid. Some terminators come with a grounding chain for grounding the braid. If a T-connector has an open end (without a terminator), the end will reflect signals on the network and that network segment will likely stop functioning.

The maximum users per segment is 30. The minimum length of the cable between T-connectors is 1.5 feet. Standards do not allow any cable between the T-connector and the equipment.

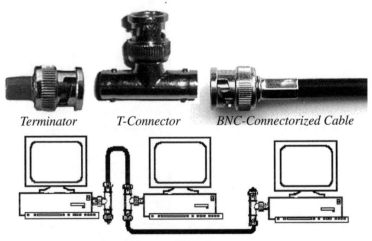

Terminator   T-Connector   BNC-Connectorized Cable

Older Ring/Daisy Chain Networks

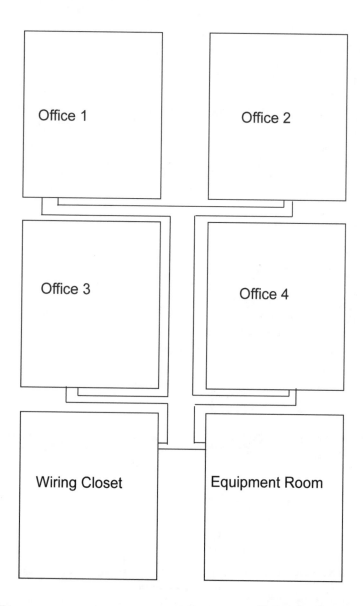

Older Ring/Daisy Chain Networks

2 or 4 Pair, UTP or STP; Application Dependent
Maximum Distance Per Run: Application Dependent
Maximum Users on network: Application Dependent

There are too many types of older STP and UTP ring and daisy chain networks to individually cover each one.

Most work done on these aging networks will be service work (such as adding a few stations, or repairing cable runs). By far the best way to perform work on these networks is to **look at the existing cabling**. Identify the jack wiring scheme from a working station, and note the LAN topology. Then add new cables as needed. Remember to keep it as neat as possible and comply with fire ratings.

The term *legacy system* describes a system that is obsolete, but a company has spent so much money on it that they do not want to upgrade to a modern network system. These networks usually have many quirks that are well documented by the computer support people at the company, so work closely with them if necessary when troubleshooting cabling.

The ring topology used to have the advantage of short cable runs, fault tolerance, and manufacturer support. The largest disadvantage was the difficulty of adding new stations. Star wired networks are far more fault tolerant than ring networks.

Even though many ring networks are fault tolerant to losing one cable run, do not unplug active connections unless you are **sure** it will not interrupt network traffic.

Note that the difference between the ring topology and the daisy chain topology is one link between the two ends of the daisy chain topology.

How Ethernet Works & CSMA/CD

CSMA/CD Stands for carrier sense, multiple access and collision detect. Only one station can be transmitting information at a time on an Ethernet segment. Therefore, all the cables in one segment of a network should theoretically have the same voltage on them at any given time (although the speed of electricity doesn't allow this to happen).

When a station needs to transmit information:

1   It senses whether there is traffic on the network cable.
2   If the cable is idle, the computer transmits packets of information. The beginning of each packet has a header that tells the address of the computer the data is being sent to. Every device has its own unique address.
3   The hub receives the packet, and repeats it back out to every port in the hub.
4   Every computer on the network receives the packet, and determines whether it was intended for itself. If the packet was not sent to it, the information is ignored.

Carrier sense is the action of a Network Interface Card (NIC) determining whether there is currently traffic on the network. *Multiple access* means all of the devices on the network share common cabling.

If two computers on an Ethernet network need to transmit information, and they both detect the cable is idle, and they both transmit at the same time, a *collision* occurs. When this happens, both of the computers that tried to transmit then wait random number of milliseconds and try to transmit again. Collisions are a normal occurrence on the network and they are not a problem until they become very frequent. *Collision detect* is the ability of the network adaptor to detect that a collision has occurred and to ignore the resulting garbled information.

Network Designations

10Base-T

10 Megabits Per Second

1	1 Megabit Per Second
10	10 Megabits Per Second
100	100 Megabits Per Second
1000	1 Gigabit Per Second

Twisted Pair Cabling

T	Twisted Pair
2	Thin Coax (185 Meters Max.)
5	Thick Coax (500 Meters Max.)
36	RG-59 Coax (3600 Meters Max.)
F	Fiber Optic

Baseband Signaling

Base	Baseband Signaling
Broad	Broadband Signaling

Network Architecture Example #1

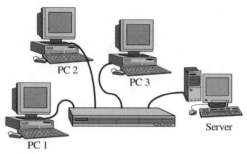

This diagram shows a simple workgroup network. Please note that required cross-connects and work area outlets are not shown. Also this is not to scale.

The network shown is a 10Base-T network with a shared hub. If PC 1 needs to send information to the server, it waits for the network to be idle. When the network is idle, it transmits packets of information, and the hub redistributes these packets to every computer on the network. Since the packets have the server's address on them, PC 2 and PC 3 ignore the packets. This is the basic way shared Ethernet works.

The part of the network shown is called a segment, or collision domain. All the cables on an Ethernet segment are supposed to have the same electrical signal on them at all times. When a computer sends information, all the computers in the segment receive it. When too many computers are connected on one segment, the network slows because all of the computers have to share the same cabling.

If this network has too much traffic, the network administrator might replace the shared hub with a multiport switch. The switch stores information about which computer address is connected to each port. Then, when the switch receives packets of information, it knows which port to send the information to. This turns the above network from one segment into four segments, with each segment only between each computer and the switch.

There is a maximum channel distance of 100 meters (328 feet) between each computer and the hub. However, as explained on page 110, the TIA/EIA-568-A standard splits the 100 meters into 3/90/7 meter distances.

The above diagram was created with NetDraw Plus software.

Mounting Methods

Stand-alone hubs sit on a table or shelf. They are most commonly used for home or small office but are also used as quick fixes in large commercial installations. *Rackmounted* hubs install on a 19" rack and are the most popular for large installations.

Eight Port, Stand-alone, Shared, Non-Managed 10Base-T Hub.

Stackable

Many hubs come with provisions to connect to other hubs from that manufacturer, enabling several hubs to function as a single logical hub.

Management

A *managed* hub lets the network administrator check the hub's status and configure the hub from a remote station through the network.

Speed

Hubs or switches can be purchased for 10 megabits per second, 100 megabits per second, or even 1000 megabits per second speeds. Some switches automatically detect the speed of a port, and these are usually called 10/100 or 10/100/1000 types.

Modular or Fixed

Most hubs have a fixed amount of ports, while modular hubs have a variable number. A modular hub is constructed with a several slots and a backplane card that has a connector at the back of each slot. Modular cards are installed in each slot. They may have, for example, 16 shared 100Base-T ports or four switched fiber ports.

Network Architecture Example #2

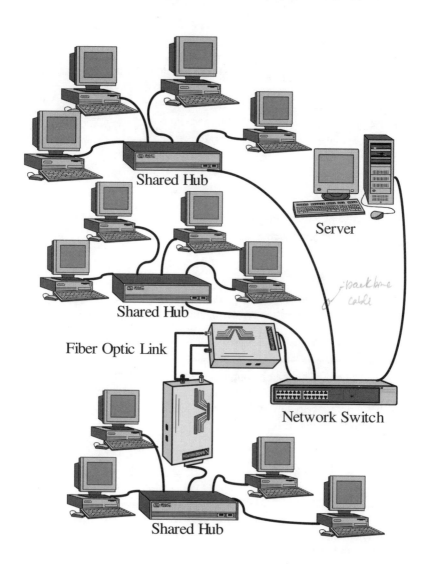

Shared Hub

Server

Shared Hub

backbone
cable

Fiber Optic Link

Network Switch

Shared Hub

This diagram was created with Network World's NetDraw Plus software.

Network Architecture Example #2

The network architecture example to the left may be typical of many different types of offices. Remember that each of the hubs can connect many more computers than shown.

The IEEE standard describing Ethernet (802.3) allows up to 328 feet (100 meters) for each backbone channel. This distance can be extended with repeaters. Each repeater extends the maximum distance by 328 feet. There are special rules that apply to the use of repeaters, look into a basic network architecture book for more information.

The cables between each hub are called backbone cables. Each twisted pair backbone link can be up to 295 feet (90m) according to article 5.5.1 of the TIA/EIA-568-A standard. The maximum fiber optic backbone length is 6560 feet (2000m) for 62.5/125 micron fiber (multimode), or 9840 feet (3000m) for singlemode fiber. Network architecture example #2 is shown without cross-connects and work area cabling for clarity.

As you can see in the diagram, fiber optic links can be connected with a media converter or transceiver. The media convertor and transceiver perform the same function as they connect fiber optic to UTP, coax to UTP, coax to fiber optic, etc. The difference between a media convertor and a transceiver is the media convertor has circuitry that regenerates signals with less noise than a transceiver. The media convertor or transceiver can be attached to the hub or switch via a UTP link, a thin coax link, or a D-shell connector 15 pin AUI cable.

When cabling between hubs, a basic principle of twisted pair Ethernet must be remembered. One pair of UTP is used for transmitting, and another for a receiving. If you are connecting two hubs, you can not just plug a patch cable between two normal ports as this connects the transmit pair from one hub to the transmit on the other, this is like two mouths but no ears. There are three simple ways to overcome this problem. 1. You can make a crossover patch cable, which transposes the transmit and receive pairs. To make a crossover cable, terminate one end of a UTP patch cord with the T568A pattern and the other end with the T568B pattern. 2. Many hubs have a special crossover port, in which case you connect a normal patch cord from this port to a normal port on the other hub. 3. You can buy special stackable hubs, which have proprietary interfaces to connect with other hubs from that manufacturer.

Chapter 7

Advanced Testing & Theory

Introduction

This chapter focuses on cable performance testing, but it also touches on necessary cable theory.

Problems you learn in this chapter affect the performance of a cable. They are not diagnosed with a continuity tester such as the Siemon STM-8. The testers needed to test cable for these problems typically cost between one and five thousand dollars.

All through this book you have seen references to excessive pair untwist. This has been to protect the signals on the cable from certain types of interference discussed in this chapter. The technician can do much to prevent most of these problems by following installation practices explained in chapter 9.

New Terms in this Chapter

Impedance Mismatch

A condition where the conductors of a pair do not have the same impedance. This is commonly caused by damaged conductors.

Nominal Velocity of Propagation (NVP)

The speed in which a voltage change propagates (travels) along a cable.

Impedance

Characteristic Impedance

A cable's *characteristic impedance* is its total obstruction to the flow of signals in each pair. Characteristic impedance is commonly confused with DC resistance, since both are measured in OHMs. Characteristic impedance is a function of resistance and reactance. *Reactance* is the effect of a conductor's signals being altered due to inductance and capacitance.

Resistance Problems

When electrons come upon a change in the resistance of a cable, a certain amount reflect back towards the source of the voltage. When this happens so much as to hinder data flow through the network, it is known as packet reflection. Also, when the impedance of two balanced conductors is not the same (likely because one conductor is damaged), signals from the cable can be radiated as radio frequency (RF) energy.

Inductance Problems

Since inductance hinders signal quality, a split pair causes havoc on the characteristic impedance of the cable. Excessive crosstalk also can cause an impedance test to fail.

Capacitance Problems

Damage to a cable will also alter the capacitance of a cable. Mutual capacitance (capacitance between the two conductors of a pair, measured in picofarads (pF)) is affected by this damage, and mutual capacitance is a factor in the determination of a cable's characteristic impedance.

When reading figures such as *100 OHM UTP* and *50 OHM COAX*, these are the characteristic impedances. The actual DC resistance of these cables is tiny in comparison.

Crosstalk

Crosstalk is the induction of current between pairs. Small amounts of crosstalk are always present between any two pairs placed near each other, but pair twisting and balanced signals were made to minimize crosstalk. Excessive crosstalk results from deformed pair twists or unbalanced signals.

Deformed pair twists are caused mostly by installation mistakes, since cables are performance tested before leaving the factory. Exceeding the bend radius and untwisting too much at terminations are the most common causes of excess crosstalk. It can also be caused by stripping back too much of the cable jackets at terminations or using components with inferior ratings. Follow installation practices in chapter nine to minimize deformed pair twists and reduce crosstalk.

Twisted pair cables carry balanced signals. Signals are balanced when the tip and ring have electrically inverse voltages. This means the same signal is flowing in both directions at the same time. Induction is mostly cancelled out with these inverse voltages. Untwisting degrades cable performance by separating the signals that are supposed to cancel each other out. Also unbalanced signals will result if there is a split pair (see page 191).

Near End Crosstalk (NEXT) & Far End Crosstalk (FEXT)

Near end crosstalk refers to crosstalk that occurs at the termination on the end of the cable near to the testing device. Far end crosstalk refers to crosstalk at the termination on the far end of the cable relative to the tester.

Signal Rate Vs. Data Rate

Subtitled: Megabits Vs. Megahertz

Signal Rate

The signal rate is the rate at which the electrical signal in the cable fluctuates. This is measured in megahertz (MHz). One megahertz is one million cycles per second.

Data Rate

The data rate is the rate at which data bits are transmitted over the network. This is measured in Megabits Per Second (mbps). One megabit equals roughly one million bits (a bit is a binary 1 or 0 value).

Comparing the Two

For older networking systems, such as 10Base-T Ethernet, the signal rate equalled the data rate. With 10Base-T, there was a 10 megahertz signal rate and a 10 megabits per second data rate.

Newer systems, such as 155 Mbps asynchronous transfer mode (ATM), have a higher efficiency of transmission. The signals in 155 Mbps ATM are transmitted at an average of roughly 85 MHz. This faster transmission is accomplished from different means of encoding. Encoding is the method that signals are sent over the network, such as whether the data is sent as a square wave (baseband), or a modulated carrier (broadband). Different square waves and modulated carrier waves have different specific efficiencies.

Testing Crosstalk: Pair to Pair VS Power Sum

Pair to pair crosstalk testing is the measure of the amount interference inducted between two pairs of a cable. Power sum crosstalk is the measure of the amount of crosstalk between three pairs and one. Power sum is a more accurate means of testing for current and future network architectures that utilize all four pairs of the cable. However, current cable testers that use pair to pair crosstalk testing still comply with TIA/EIA TSB-67, the document which outlines specifications for field cable performance testers.

Signal Direction

There are three terms that describe the direction that data is transmitted on a cable. These are commonly used to describe data flow in a cable.

Simplex
Data only flows in one direction.
Half Duplex
Data flows in both directions, but only one at a time.
Full Duplex
Data flows in both directions at the same time. This obviously requires multiple conductors (or fibers).

Note that these describe data flow, not signal flow. In a balanced pair, electrical current is flowing in opposite directions at any given point and time. This is considered full duplex signaling, but half duplex data flow since data is only sent in one direction (at a time).

EMI/RFI Interference

Electromagnetic Interference (EMI) and Radio Frequency Interference (RFI) are signals (stray current) inducted onto the cable from external sources. Unlike crosstalk, which is induction between pairs, EMI/RFI comes from outside sources such as motors, high voltage power lines, lamp ballasts, and poorly shielded computer equipment.

Excessive EMI/RFI can be more dangerous than crosstalk, since a high amount of voltage inducted onto the cable can harm network electronics using the cable.

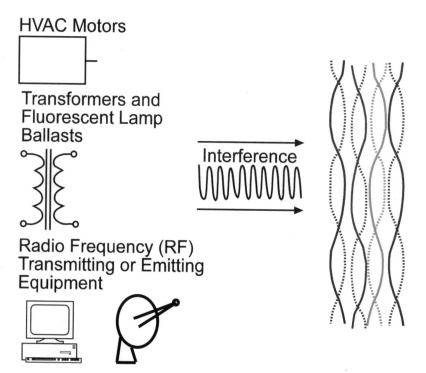

HVAC Motors

Transformers and Fluorescent Lamp Ballasts

Interference

Radio Frequency (RF) Transmitting or Emitting Equipment

Fluke DSP-2000

The Fluke DSP-2000 (shown at left) is a cabling performance tester. It has advanced auto-diagnostics that graphically pinpoint problems in installed cabling. The DSP-2000 will save up to 1,150 test results, and they can be downloaded to a computer and printed. The recharge-able NiCad battery typically has a 10-12 hour life.

The DSP-2000 also contains a traffic monitor for 10Base-T and 100Base-T networks. This monitor will diagnose basic cabling faults that prevent network operation, in addition to showing current traffic/utilization percentages of the network.

Datacom LANcat System 6

The Datacom LANcat System 6 tests cabling performance. It has all of the standard perfor-mance tester features, plus some extra features that can prove valuable to field technicians. Both the base and remote units have graphic LCDs to make troubleshooting easier. A talkset is integrated in each unit, these allow technicians to talk to eachother through unused cable pairs.

The WaveTek LanTek

The WaveTek LanTek is a performance tester. It can perform a whole suite of tests that are used to test new installations, or troubleshoot problems in existing ones.

The LanTek has a simple, menu driven user interface for simple use. Extensive training on its use is not required.

An advantage of many performance testers is their ability to retain tests in memory. The LanTek base can be connected to a computer or printer so the installers can provide their customers with printed reports of the cable test.

Performance testers provide the installer with the cable length, a feature that is handy for billing purposes and evaluating compliance with standards.

The LanTek has a 15 pin D-shell connectors and BNC connectors for cable connection. The 15 pin connector is in place of a UTP jack. A short adapter cable is provided to connect UTP. This method is used so when the UTP jack wears out, a new adapter cable can be used instead of requiring internal repair to the LanTek.

The LanTek operates with a base unit and a remote. Both of the units use the same battery, but the remote has a longer battery life. Both the base and the remote can have their firmware (program memory) updated through a 9-pin serial cable connection.

Performance Tests

Autotest
The autotest runs the wiremap, length, attenuation, and NEXT tests. These four tests alone will diagnose the performance of the cable.

Wiremap
Tests the continuity of each of the eight conductors and shows a graphical representation of the continuity.

Length
Displays the length of each pair.

Attenuation
Tests the cable attenuation and displays results in dB (loss).

Dual NEXT
Tests the cable's near end crosstalk with the main unit and the remote unit. Since it tests the NEXT on both ends, it is called Dual NEXT.

Mutual Capacitance
Tests the mutual capacitance of the cable and displays the results in picofarads (pF).

Time Domain Reflectometer (TDR)
Injects power onto the cable and measures power reflected from changes in impedance. This is very useful in locating damage to a cable.

Loop Resistance
Measures the overall resistance of a cable.

Troubleshooting Failures

Example 1.

You just finished a test on a cable you installed, and the tester displays:

Linemap:	Fail
Length:	Pass
Impedance:	Fail
Dual NEXT:	Fail

This output is characteristic of an open conductor. Do not even look at the impedance or NEXT failures, because they are both most likely caused by the linemap failure. Examine both terminations, punch down each conductor again, and test it again.

Example 2.

Your next test displays:

Linemap:	Pass
Length:	Pass
Impedance:	Pass
Dual NEXT:	Fail

In this situation, it is most likely one of the ends has too much untwist on the termination. Test it again after cutting off the cable and punching it down again.

If that doesn't fix it, look and make sure the cable jacket has been maintained as close as possible to the termination point. If it still fails, your problem is likely to be an installation mistake along the cable run. Make sure you followed all of the installation practices in chapter 9. Before you give up and pull another cable, try another jack or patch panel port.

The cable must be at least fifteen meters long to perform the NEXT test properly. If the cable is shorter, it may fail NEXT.

Example 3.

Another cable test might display:

Linemap:	Pass
Length:	Pass
Impedance:	Fail
Dual NEXT:	Pass

In this case, it is most likely that cutting off one end of the cable and punching it down again will fix the problem. If it doesn't fix the problem, suspect that the jack or port on the patch panel may be defective.

Other Notes

Make sure that you calibrate the tester regularly, according to its manufacturer's instructions. If you believe the indicated cable length is incorrect, check the calibration of the tester's NVP (nominal velocity of propagation).

To check for cable damage along a run, try using the TDR (time domain reflectometer) function on your tester.

Certain testers give unpredictable results when their batteries are too low. This is mostly a problem with lower-cost testers.

As shown in examples 1-3, the best order to deal with problems is:
1. Length
2. Linemap
3. Crosstalk
4. Impedance

Chapter 8
Cabling Standards

Introduction

This chapter will show how standards have shaped the modern cabling industry.

New Terms in this Chapter
Standard
An industry-recognized document outlining requirements for an aspect of the industry. Cabling standards specify the types of cables and connectors that should be used, and how cable is to be installed.
Cabling System
Also known as the **Premises Distribution System** (PDS), it includes all of the cables, terminations, and cross-connects between computer equipment. It also includes the methods of installation and maintenance. Some cabling manufacturers sell complete cabling systems.
Telecommunications System Bulletin (TSB)
A paper released by the Telecommunications Industry Association (TIA) to clarify or add information to one of their major standards.

History of Standards

Pre-1984 AT&T had a monopoly over telephone cabling. Computer manufacturers each had their own way of cabling networks, often incompatible with each other.

January 1, 1984 AT&T divestiture. AT&T was split up into regional telephone, long distance, manufacturing, and research companies.

Circa 1985 Communications cabling installers and manufacturers were concerned about the lack of a standard for the *Premise Distribution System* (PDS), the building's cabling infrastructure. The Electronic Industries Association (EIA) (their name has since been changed to the Electronics Industry Alliance) was urged to develop a standard for a structured cabling system.

1991 The much-awaited standard was formally published as EIA/TIA-568.

1995 The EIA/TIA-568 standard and several telecommunications system bulletins (TSBs) were combined to make the TIA/EIA-568-A standard. This was later slightly modified and made into the internationally recognized ISO/IEC 11801 standard.

Additional TSBs and revisions can be expected in the future.

The next revision of TIA/EIA-568-A is expected to define categories above 5 and eliminate thin coaxial (RG-58) cable.

Standards and Laws

Most standards are not legal in nature. They simply outline the way the cabling should be installed in order to create a uniform, easy to upgrade, and easy to change system. Some municipalities adopt certain standards as laws, the most common example of this is the *National Fire Protection Association* (NFPA) *National Electrical Code (*NEC), that is adopted in many areas as the law for electrical installations.

Become familiar with these organizations:

National Fire Protection Association (NFPA)
Publishes the National Electrical Code (NEC), an electrocution and fire prevention standard. It is adopted as electrical code law in many local jurisdictions. The code is not a law as it is published, but most local governments adopt the NEC or parts of it as their local electrical code.

Federal Communications Commission (FCC)
Creates codes on acceptable devices for connection to the public telephone network. All codes are law.

The following federal agencies are involved in standards that are sometimes required for cabling in government or military buildings:

Occupational Safety and Health Administration (OSHA)
Federal Communications Commission (FCC)
National Technical Information Service (NTIS)
General Services Administration (GSA)

Standards Organizations

International Organization for Standardization (ISO)
Geneva, Switzerland

ISO is pronounced "I-S-O" or sometimes "I-So". The ISO was formed in 1947. It consists of 90 nations and is a group of the principle standards bodies from each country. The US member is the ANSI.

American National Standards Institute (ANSI)
11 W 42nd St, 13th Flr, New York, NY 10036. (212) 642-4900

ANSI is pronounced "Ansee". The ANSI is the main American standards body. Their standards universally reach almost all industries.

Electronic Industries Alliance (EIA)
2500 Wilson Blvd. Arlington, VA 22201-3834 (703) 907-7500

EIA is pronounced "E-I-A". The EIA develops standards for the electronics and computer industries. Many documents list the EIA as the Electronic Industries Association, but their name was changed in March of 1998. The EIA is empowered by the ANSI to make official standards relevant to the electronics industry.

Telecommunications Industry Association (TIA)
2500 Wilson Blvd., Suite 300 Arlington, VA 22201 (703) 907-7700

TIA is pronounced "T-I-A". The TIA is empowered by the ANSI to make official standards relevant to the communications industry. The goal of their standards is to produce a cabling system that supports compatibility between all cabling manufacturers' products and all network electronics.

Building Industry Consulting Service International (BICSI, *A Telecommunications Association*)
8610 Hidden River Parkway Tampa, FL 33637 (800) 242-7405

BICSI is pronounced "Bic-see". BICSI does not create standards, but they publish installer manuals that explain cabling practices. They also hold cabling system design and installation seminars, and administer the RCDD certification for communications system designers. By the end of 2000, BICSI expects to serve over 20,000 people from 85 countries.

Communications Cabling

Underwriters Laboratories (UL)

333 Pfingston Rd., Northbrook, IL 60062, (847) 272-8800

UL is pronounced "U-L". The UL is an independent testing laboratory that created a standard called the *UL LAN Cable Certification Program*.

Institute of Electrical and Electronics Engineers (IEEE)

445 Hoes Lane, Piscataway, N.J. 08854 (800)-678-4333

IEEE is pronounced "I-triple-E". They are the world's largest engineering society, consisting of over 320,000 members. The IEEE publishes standards relating to all aspects of electronics, including the 802 series of networking system standards, explained on page 105.

National Fire Protection Association (NFPA)

1 Batterymarch Park, Quincy, MA 02269-9101 (617) 770-3000

NFPA is pronounced "N-F-P-A". They publish the NFPA70, which is also known as the National Electrical Code (NEC). Many local building electrical codes are based on the NEC, so it is important to be familiar with how to use it.

The OSI Model

Layer 7:   **Application**
Layer 6:   **Presentation**
Layer 5:   **Session**
Layer 4:   **Transport**
Layer 3:   **Network**
Layer 2:   **Data Link**
Layer 1:   **Physical**

The ISO Open Systems Interconnection (ISO OSI) model was made to simplify contracting network design and services into parts of the network operation. It is far out of the scope of this book to explain every layer, so we will skip over most of the details of it.

The user's network software is in the application layer. The network cabling is the physical layer. The functioning of every layer is necessary for the transmission of data.

IEEE Standards Groups

The IEEE has many standards groups that each develop standards for a specific technology. The 802 groups deal with network standards. These standards dictate the method in which data is sent over the network, and the media and equipment used to send it. The standards include acceptable characteristics of transmission mediums (network cables). Only the most relevant groups are listed here.

802.3 CSMA/CD

Defines standards for networks using CSMA/CD, otherwise known as Ethernet. For an explanation of CSMA/CD refer to page 80.

802.5 Token Ring

Defines how data can be passed over a ring topology using a token passing technology.

802.11 Wireless LANs

Defines how data can be passed using wireless methods, including spread spectrum, microwave, and infrared transmission.

802.12 100VG-AnyLAN

Defines how 100 Megabits-per-second transmission can be achieved using four pair Category 3 cabling.

ANSI/TIA/EIA-568-A
Commercial Building Telecommunications Cabling Standard

ANSI/EIA/TIA-569-A
Commercial Building Standards for Telecommunications Pathways and Spaces

ANSI/EIA/TIA-570
Residential and Light Commercial Telecommunications Wiring Standard

ANSI/TIA/EIA-606
The Administration Standard for the Telecommunications Infrastructure of Commercial Buildings

ANSI/TIA/EIA-607
Commercial Building Grounding and Bonding Requirements for Telecommunications

ANSI/TIA/EIA TSB 67
Transmission Performance Specifications for Field Testing of Twisted-Pair Cabling Systems

ANSI/TIA/EIA TSB 72
Centralized Optical Fiber Cabling Guidelines

ANSI/TIA/EIA TSB 95
Additional Transmission Performance Guidelines for 4-Pair 100 Ohm Category 5 Cable

Acquiring Copies of Standards

Copies of these standards can be purchased from Global Engineering Documents at 1-800-854-7179. At the time of this writing, purchasing all of these standards together costs $475.

Premises Distribution Systems

The Premises Distribution System (PDS) is the entire cabling system in a building. The TIA/EIA-568-A standard covers all six sections of the PDS, and they are summarized here. Note that the standard calls for up to two levels of interconnects to connect telecommunications closets (TC). These two levels are called the intermediate cross-connect (IC) and the main cross-connect (MC). WAO stands for work area outlet. Any of the cross-connects can be located in equipment rooms.

MC
IC   IC ←—— First Level Backbone
←—— Second Level Backbone
TC TC TC TC
WAO   WAO |←—Horizontal Cable
WAO WAO WAO

A. Entrance Facilities

The point in a building where cables enter the building. At this place the cables from outside the building meet with the backbone cable inside the building. Outside cables must be spliced (using cross-connects) at the building entrance facility.

B. Equipment Room

Equipment rooms usually house more equipment than normally found in a telecommunications closet. They typically function as an IC or the MC. Physical specifications for equipment rooms are contained in the TIA/EIA-569-A standard.

C. Backbone Cabling

Connects telecommunication closets, entrance facilities and equipment rooms. Cables are generally referred to as backbone if they carry the information of more than one user.

PDS Diagram

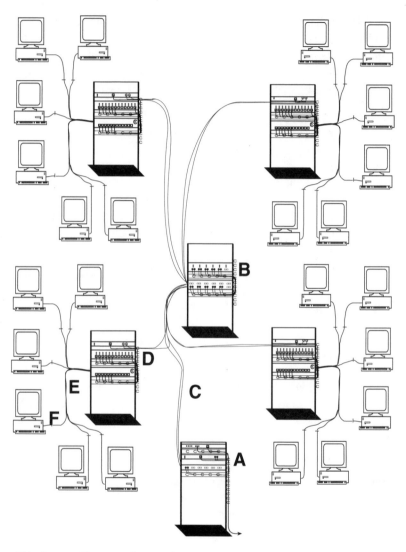

This diagram illustrates the six subsystems as described on pages 107 and 109.

D. Telecommunications Closets

The telecommunications closet houses cabling distribution equipment. You will usually find cross-connect blocks and hubs in telecommunications closets. A backbone cable connects equipment in the telecommunications closet to equipment in the intermediate distribution frame.

E. Horizontal Cabling

The horizontal cabling is the individual run from the work area outlet to the telecommunications closet. This section of the cabling includes the horizontal cabling, the work area jack, the termination to the cross-connect in the telecommunications closet. Horizontal cable exists above permanent or drop ceilings, through walls, raceway, and in conduit. It does not normally penetrate concrete floors or exterior walls. The total distance from the user equipment to the hub may be 100 meters. This breaks down to 90 meters between the work area outlet and the cross-connect block, 3 meters from the work area outlet to the user equipment, and 7 meters in the telecommunications closet, but with a maximum single patch cord length of six meters.

F. Work Area

Work area cables are the simple patch cords between the equipment and the work area outlet. Patch cords must carry the rating of the cabling system. For example, if you are installing a Category 5 compliant cabling system, you must use Category 5 patch cords. Any adapters or splitters must be external to the outlet. Work area cabling should be simple enough for end users to move without technical assistance.

According to article 4.5 of the TIA/EIA-568-A standard, a minimum of two cables are pulled to each work area. One is meant for voice and the other for data. These two cables terminate to two separate modular jacks, which are both mounted on one outlet plate. A work area is considered 100 square feet, so if a room is larger, plan for multiple work area outlets. Category 5 cabling is recommended for all new installations.

The cable for voice is:

√ Four pair, AWG 24, 100 ohm UTP, Category 3 minimum

The second cable, for data, is a choice of (at least) one of the following:

√ Four pair, AWG 24, 100 ohm UTP, Category 3 minimum

√ Two pair, 150 Ohm STP

√ Two Strand, 62.5/125 µm Fiber Optic

TIA/EIA-568-A Maximum Cable Distances

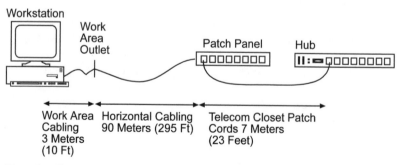

Note that the maximum length for a single telecom closet patch cord is six meters. Refer to article 4.3 in the TIA/EIA-568-A standard for more information.

Cable Separation Distances

To protect cables from EMI/RFI and for safety concerns, cables must be separated from certain electrical power lines. The chart at right shows required separation distances.

At the bottom are additional restrictions to observe when running cable.

Note: Both of the illustrations on this page are reprinted with permission from the publication "Voice & Data Wiring Strategies," copyright Leviton Telcom.

Purpose	Type of Wire Involved	Minimum Separation
Electric Supply	Bare light or power of any voltage.	5 feet
	Open wiring not over 300 volts.	2 inches
	Wires in conduit, or in armored or non-metallic sheath cable/power ground wires.	None
Radio & TV	Antenna lead & ground wires without grounded shield.	4 inches
Signal/ Control Wire	Open wiring not over 300 volts.	None
CATV Cables	Community television systems coaxial cables with grounded shield.	None
Telephone Service Drop Wire	Aerial or buried.	2 inches
Sign	Neon signs and associated wiring from transformer.	6 inches
Fluorescent Lighting	Fluorescent lighting wire.	5 inches
Lightning System	Lightning rods and wires.	6 feet

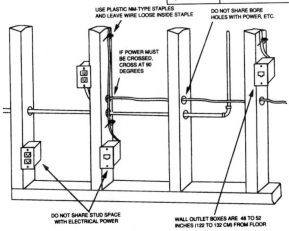

USE PLASTIC NM-TYPE STAPLES AND LEAVE WIRE LOOSE INSIDE STAPLE

DO NOT SHARE BORE HOLES WITH POWER, ETC.

IF POWER MUST BE CROSSED, CROSS AT 90 DEGREES

DO NOT SHARE STUD SPACE WITH ELECTRICAL POWER

WALL OUTLET BOXES ARE 48 TO 52 INCHES (122 TO 132 CM) FROM FLOOR

Telecommunication Closets

The telecommunications closet (TC) contains equipment for both telecommunications (telecom) and data communications (datacom) equipment.

The TIA/EIA-568-A standard:

√ Horizontal: Allows up to seven meters of patch cords in the telecommunications closet, but no patch cord can be longer than six meters.

√ Backbone: If the backbone link is 90 meters, then the maximum patch cord length is 5 meters at each end.

The TIA/EIA-569-A standard:

√ Closet sizing according to the sizing table at right (recommended sizes).

√ There must be a minimum of one closet per floor.

EIA/TIA-569-A Recommended TC Sizing	
Area Served	Closet Size
10000 Sq. Ft.	10' x 11'
8000 Sq. Ft.	10' x 9'
5000 Sq. Ft.	10' x 7'

√ Multiple closets should be made when the area served exceeds 10,000 sq. ft. or the distance from the closet to a work area exceeds 295 feet (90 meters).

√ The closet must have a minimum door width of 36" and must have a lock.

√ A minimum of two 120V 20A dedicated power circuits must be provided for active equipment. Make provisions for outages.

√ The climate control system must be available at all times, even when power outages occur.

112

Labeling Installations

Methods of cabling system documentation are contained in the TIA/EIA-606 standard. Refer to this standard for complete information on how to document a cabling system, as this is only an overview.

When labeling cable installations:

√ Label both ends of horizontal and backbone cables.

√ It is preferable to attach a tag or label rather than write on the cable.

√ Use a complete system of identifiers and record-keeping as explained in the TIA/EIA-606 standard.

The following are color codes to help identify parts of the cabling system. These color codes are for labeling purposes, they are not necessarily the color of the equipment or cable jacket. The *Pantone Matching System* is a printing industry standard that helps commercial printers and customers communicate exact shades of color.

COLOR	PANTONE	TERMINATION TYPE
Orange	150C	Demarcation Point (see chapter 11)
Green	353C	Network connections on the customer side of the demarcation point.
Purple	264C	Connections to common equipment, such as PBXs or multiplexers.
White	-	Connections between the main cross-connect and intermediate cross-connects.
Gray	422C	Connections between the intermediate cross-connect and the telecommunications closet.
Blue	291C	Horizontal cable terminations.
Brown	465C	Backbones between buildings.
Yellow	101C	Other circuits, such as maintenance controls, alarms.
Red	184C	Key telephone connections.

Excerpted from table 8.3-1 in the TIA/EIA-606 standard.

Manufacturers' Cabling Systems

Many large cabling and component manufacturers will guarantee an entire system that is installed with their products for many years. The term *structured cabling* refers to a cabling system that is made exclusively of standard components from a manufacturer's cabling system, and installed to the TIA/EIA-568-A standard.

Different manufacturers have varied qualification criteria for an installed system to get their warranty. The following are the most common requirements to qualify for these warranties:

√   The installation company (and/or the installer themselves) must be certified by the manufacturer.

√   The cabling system must be installed to TIA standards.

√   The cabling system must be Category 5 performance tested.

√   The whole system must only use components from approved manufacturers.

Below is a table of several manufacturers and their cabling systems:

Manufacturer	Cabling System	Warranty
Lucent Technologies	Systimax	15 Years
Leviton Telcom	GigaMax	Lifetime
Hubbell Premise Wiring	Hubbell Premise	15 Years
Krone & Belden	Symphony Warranty Program	20 Years
NORDX/CDT	IBDN	15 Years

NEC Cable Terms & Ratings

Plenum

Plenum areas are defined in the National Electrical Code (NEC) article 100 as "A compartment or chamber to which one or more air ducts are connected and that forms part of the air distribution system." Section 800-53 requires that "Cables installed in ducts, plenums, and other spaces used for environmental air shall be type CMP." Areas meeting this definition commonly exist above drop ceilings and below computer room floors, so survey an area carefully before installing cable.

Riser

A riser is a vertical run or shaft that penetrates the floors of a building. Riser rated cable jacket is resistant to carrying flames vertically. As with all other fire-barriers, penetrations between building floors must be fire-stopped, as stated in NEC section 300-21.

CM Rated Cable

Communications cable. These are usually made with a PVC (polyvinyl chloride) jacket. CM cables may not be used in plenum or riser areas. Some exceptions may apply to cable in conduit, in accordance with NEC section 300-22. Consult the NEC and local codes for more information.

CMR Rated Cable

Communications Riser cable. CMR can be substituted for CM cable.

CMP Rated Cable

Communications Plenum cable. Plenum cables are special in that they are fire-resistant and must reach a higher temperature before emitting toxic smoke. The most common material for the plenum-rated jacket is Dupont Teflon FEP (fluorinated ethylene propylene). Plenum rated cable can be substituted in place of CMR or CM cable. To save time and effort, many cabling companies pay extra to buy only CMP cable, to simplify purchasing and to eliminate the need to judge whether an area requires plenum rated cable.

Quoted information on this page is reprinted with permission from NFPA 70-1999, the *National Electrical Code*®, Copyright© 1998, National Fire Protection Association, Quincy, MA 02269. This reprinted material is not the complete and official position of the National Fire Protection Association, on the referenced subject which is represented only by the standard in its entirety.

Chapter 9
Installing Cable

Introduction

This chapter covers many issues relating to installing cable properly. The methods in this chapter will help you to install cable to pass Category 5 testing and to be compliant with major cabling system standards.

All of the installation practices shown apply for Category 5E as well as Category 5.

New Terms in this Chapter
Fire-stopping

Fire-stopping is preserving the integrity of a fire barrier. It can be accomplished with special putty, caulk, pipe sections, and/or other means. Fire barriers commonly include, but are not limited to, firewalls, exterior walls, and poured concrete floors.

Cabling Methods to Avoid

Twists & Knots

Do not allow cables to become kinked or knotted. This happens most often when pulling cable out of boxes. Follow instructions on the cable box to help avoid kinks and knots.

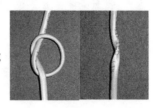

Cable Supports

Do not overload cable hooks, clips or rings to the point of putting stress on cables.

Cable Ties

Do not cinch cables or overtighten cable ties. Many installers prefer velcro-type cable ties.

Staples

Do not crush the cable under a staple.

Cabling Methods to Avoid

Pulling Tension

Do not exert more than 25 pounds of pulling force on a cable during installation.

Bending Cable

Route cables with wide curves. Do not kink excessive bends into the cable. Bend the cable at a radius that is four times the diameter of the jacket (10X cable diameter for 25+ pair cables). For example, a cable with 3/16" jacket diameter should have a maximum bend of 3/4" radius.

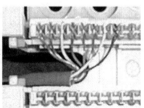

Termination Untwist

The maximum untwist length for Category 5 systems is 1/2". For Category 4, the maximum untwist length is 1". The number is unspecified for Category 3, but 3" should be safe.

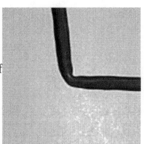

Missing Jacket

Do not strip the cable jacket past where needed for termination.

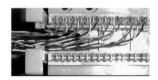

Follow these rules to help ensure a proper installation that will pass performance testing, comply with standards, and provide the customer with a long lasting, easy to manage cabling system.

Splices

Do not splice a cable between the work area outlet and the telecommunications closet. If a cable breaks or is too short, pull a new cable.

Test Cable

Test your installation with a continuity tester or preferably with a performance tester before calling a job complete. Many contracts require performance tests on Category 5 cabling.

Label Outlets

Label outlets according to the TIA/EIA-606 standard. Make sure the labeling is simple enough for the user to understand (label "voice" & "data" if necessary).

Electrical Power

Follow the separation table on page 111 to avoid interference from outside sources. There is no separation required from shielded & grounded power cables (i.e. most of those in separate conduit or metallic armor).

Heat & Sunlight

Avoid running cable near heat sources like hot water or steam pipes, or anywhere that exposes the cable to direct sunlight.

Wiring Configuration

Wire jacks for the configuration specified by the customer. Maintain one pattern throughout the entire installation.

Installing Cable Properly

Staples

Do not tightly staple wires.

Pull Cords

If it is convenient, pull a pull line along with your cable. Always leave a pull line in conduits.

Under Carpet Installations

Avoid installing cable under carpets. If you have to run undercarpet cables, make sure the cable is properly rated for this use.

Bend Radius

Do not bend cables sharply. The minimum bend radius is 4X the jacket diameter for four pair cables, and 10X for 25+ pairs.

External Wires

External wires run outside of the building. Although they are allowed in many local codes, this practice should not be done for original installations and avoided for additions.

Service Loop

Leave several feet of cable behind an outlet box to accommodate re-terminations. However, do not cram cable into the outlet box.

Fire-Stopping

Always fire-stop penetrations to any floor, firewall, exterior wall, or other fire-barrier. If a fire happens and the fire inspector finds that a fire spread through a penetration that an installer left unprotected, the installer's company may be held responsible for the damage.

Placing Outlets

The separation table on page 111 also applies for separation between electrical outlets & communication outlets. Place communication outlets at the same height on the wall as electrical outlets.

Furniture Layout

The maximum work area patch cord length in the TIA/EIA-568-A standard is under 10 feet. Place two outlets in an office (two cable runs, do **not** bridge the outlets together) if the user's equipment might be placed too far away from an outlet. It is far easier to do this in the original installation than in later service calls.

Document Installations

If a blueprint is not already drawn up for the installation, make a map of all the outlets with their port numbers (or cabling system identifiers). Follow TIA/EIA-606.

Pull Force

Do not pull on four pair UTP cable with a force of more than 25 pounds. Exceeding this will stretch and damage the cable. For other cable types, check their manufacturer's rating.

Painters

When installing in newly constructed or renovated areas, either install outlets after walls are painted, or make sure they are masked properly so the painters don't destroy your outlets.

Punching Jacks

When terminating modular jacks, DO NOT place the back of the jack against the wall when punching it down. The impact from the punch tool will cause the jack to leave dents in the wall.

NEXT Loss

The table below can help you gauge the effects of different problems on a Category 5 installation.

Action Applied to Channel	NEXT Performance Reduction
Full Channel, Properly Installed	Benchmark
Cable flexed 1000 times	No Change
Replace 2 ft Cat 5 patch cord with 2 ft Cat 3	8.0 dB
Replace 20 ft Cat 5 patch cord with 20 ft Cat 3	13.0 dB
Coiled cable in 6' circle, 2" dia. cross section	No Change
Bundled & secured cable with cable ties	No Change
Removed 1" of cable sheath at station end	1.2 dB
Removed 12" of cable sheath at station end	2.0 dB
Untwisted pairs 1/2" at station end	1.5 dB
Untwisted pairs 2" at station end	3.8 dB
Untwisted pairs 6" at station end	11.6 dB
Bend cable around 3" diameter	1.9 dB
Bend cable around a 1" diameter	2.1 dB
Kinked cable	2.4 dB
Cable run in aluminum conduit	No Change

Note: This table was reprinted with permission from the Leviton Telcom publication, "Voice & Data Wiring Strategies."

Cable Jacket Markings

Comtran Corp

This is the cable's manufacturer.

24 AWG

The conductor size is 24 gauge on the American Wire Gauge (AWG).

Type MPP/CMP

The National Electrical Code (NEC) designation for this cable is
Multipurpose Plenum (MPP) and Communications Plenum (CMP).

Verified Cat 3

The cable has been verified to Category 3 specifications.

Tested to 350 MHZ

The cable has been tested to perform within certain tolerances at up to
350 MHZ. The special mention is due to the fact that there is no official
standard of cable testing above 100 MHZ.

283,918 FT

Foot marking. This marking is relative to the spool it comes on. In
this case, a 1,000 foot spool might start its marking at 283,000 feet and end
at 284,000 feet. The foot marking is helpful for installers to determine the
length of cable runs. For example, at the beginning of the job, the installer
might note that the end of the spool is marked 283,420, and when he's
finished installing the last mark on the spool is 283,918 ft. He can now
determine 283,918-283,420=498 feet were used on the job.

Cable Management

Cable management is an important part of any cabling installation. If proper cable management is not installed, the wiring closet will quickly turn into a nightmare of tangled cables. This is by far not a complete guide on designing cable management systems, but these descriptions will help you identify cable management (and hopefully use it).

110 Cross-connects

When using 110-type cross-connects, use either hooks or troughs guide the cable. 110 cross-connects are commonly mounted to plywood backboards, and cable troughs like those shown at right are mounted above and/or below the cross-connect.

66 Cross-connects

When using 66-type cross-connects, cable hooks and rings are the most common way of guiding cable. 66 blocks & their cable management are usually mounted onto plywood backboards.

Rackmounted Patch Panels

Cable management for 19" racks is accomplished with bolt on cable guides. Many cable guides are simply panels with rings that guide the

cable. Cable ducts like shown at left can be mounted vertically or horizontally on communications racks. The side panel is removable and cables are routed through grooves on both sides of the duct. Most any method of cable management is effective as long as it is used properly.

Cable Runways (Ladder Racks)

These fixtures look like ladders and are commonly mounted in ceilings and around telecommunications closets or equipment rooms. Cable is laid on the rack, and can be secured with cable ties. Many manufacturers have complete lines of interchangeable segments and fittings.

The pictures on this page are courtesy of Panduit.

Scope of Conduit Coverage

The conduit information in this book is provided for your general knowledge and understanding. It is by no means all of the information you need to install conduit-based distribution systems. Information here covers common installation methods, however, there are exceptions. Consult the *National Electrical Code* and local building codes for more information.

EMT Conduit

Electrical Metallic Tubing (EMT) is the most common type of conduit for electrical and communications installations.

EMT Fitting

Connects EMT to a pull box, device box, splice box, or distribution panel.

EMT Coupling

Connects two pieces of EMT together. These are not pull points.

Pulling Elbow

These connect two pieces of conduit in a 90 degree bend while providing a pull point. These far exceed allowable bend radii, do NOT use these for communications cabling.

Innerduct

This flexible, nonmetallic plastic tubing is commonly pulled inside of ductwork to protect fiber optic or copper-based cabling. It usually comes with a pull string pre-installed, as shown.

EMT Installation Methods

Set Screw Couplings

EMT is inserted in both ends and the screws are tightened. These are very common since EMT comes in ten foot lengths.

One-Hole Straps

These mount conduit to walls and backboards. EMT must be supported at least once every ten feet, and within at least 3 feet of either side of a pull box or coupling.

Conduit Bending

Conduit bending is accomplished with a conduit bending tool, or buying preformed bends. Bends must be gradual and not distort the internal shape of the conduit.

Pull Boxes

Cables may not be spliced in a pull box. According to TIA/EIA-569-A, there must be a pull box for every 100 feet of conduit, 180 degrees (two right angles), or U-shaped bend.

Conduit Fill Rates

Per table 4.4-1 in the TIA/EIA-569-A standard, this table shows the maximum number of cables that can be installed in a conduit.

Conduit Trade Size	Maximum Number of Cables With This Diameter				
	.18"	.24"	.37"	.53"	.70"
16 (1/2")	1	0	0	0	0
21 (3/4")	5	3	1	0	0
27 (1")	8	6	2	1	0
103 (4")	-	-	30	14	7

Using Surface Mount Raceway

Note that information on this page is a summary of the applicable rules for installation; consult the appropriate documents and codes for more information.

According to TIA/EIA-569-A, the following guidelines must be followed when installing surface mount raceways:

√   Raceways should only be filled to between 20-40% of capacity.

√   Metal and nonmetal raceway should only be used in dry locations.

√   Since cables are usually installed by laying the cable in rather than fishing and pulling, the minimum bend radius is one inch.

Several companies make complete raceway systems that comply with standards. This is a 90 degree bend from Panduit's Pan-Way system.

Surface mount raceway is commonly attached to walls using pre-applied adhesive strips. If the wall is not smooth or clean enough for the adhesive to stick, screws are used to mount the raceway.

Several different kinds of surface mount raceway can be purchased. The easiest way to see all of the different kinds is to call or write for a catalog from one of the raceway manufacturers listed in appendix A.

Power and communication circuits can be run through the same raceway as long as a physical barrier is present between them. Raceway can be purchased with a suitable partition pre-installed.

Surface mount raceway should be avoided for new installations (unless a special situation requires it), but it is invaluable for adds, changes, and areas not accessible to normal cabling practices.

Surface mount raceway, such as this one from Panduit, house power and communication cables in separate chambers.

Securing & Mounting Cables

Traditionally, cable runs above ceilings have been placed directly on ceiling tiles or secured with cable ties. The result is an inefficient means of managing cables. A more efficient method of cable management is cable trays and cable runways. Both of these products provide continuous mechanical support and excellent cable management for future expansion and changes, as well as offering a means to protect your cabling.

Cable hooks can be used to support communications cabling and may be fastened to a variety of structures including beams, vertical flanges, 'Z' purlins and acoustical ceilings. Cable hooks are designed to maximize the cable-bearing surface, eliminate stress and optimize cable performance. Traditional fastening methods such as cable ties and bridle rings are not suitable for high-performance cabling because of the stress points created by these narrow-base fasteners. These stress points, coupled with excessive cable sag, result in decreased cable performance and data transmission distortion.

The above text & photographs were contributed by B-Line Systems, Inc.

Clips such as the one at right can be mounted in the work area if needed to support or route cables. It can also be used in the telecommunications closet or equipment room for the same purpose.

Chapter 10

Residential/Voice Cabling

Introduction

This chapter contains information helpful to the installer of residential and voice cabling.

New Terms in this Chapter

Demarcation Point

The point where the phone company's network ends and the customer's cabling starts. It can be a cross-connect block or special network interface box.

Residential Phone Cabling

Residential phone cabling uses two pair modular jacks. Single, analog voice lines use one pair of conductors.

Most older homes are cabled with four conductor, non-twisted pair cable. It is commonly known as *quad wire*. Never use this cable in new installations. It is unsuitable for anything other than single line, analog voice transmission. In two line voice installations that use quad wire, you can often faintly hear the conversation on the other line. This is an effect of crosstalk, and is how crosstalk got its name. With the current rush of homes to get fax and Internet services, only twisted pair cabling supports communication in the present as well as the future.

Silver satin refers to non-twisted phone patch cords that are colored silver. These are still acceptable to use for single line phone patch cords, but they are not to be used for any high speed computer communication.

As of July, 2000, the FCC amended their regulations on inside wiring that is to be connected to the public telephone network. Now, cable must be a minimum of Category 3. A summary of this order is on page 165.

Telephone color codes are on page 192.

Residential Cabling

Until recently, residential telephone cabling was always wired with non-twisted cable and in the ring topology. The poor education of some building contractors has stifled the movement in residential construction to migrate to UTP and the star topology. The most advanced of builders are now using Category 5 cable and the star topology, since they know that configuration will be useful for the longest time. In the future, the quality of a house's cabling will increasingly affect its value.

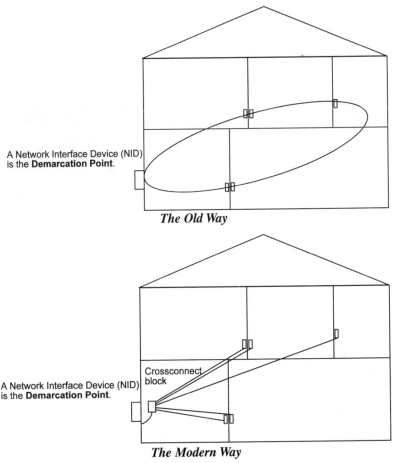

A Network Interface Device (NID)
is the **Demarcation Point**.

The Old Way

Crossconnect block

A Network Interface Device (NID)
is the **Demarcation Point**.

The Modern Way

Home Cabling Systems

One reason many construction companies are slow to start using the star topology is ignorance of how to make the central connection point. There are several ways to use generic cross-connect blocks to connect individual cable runs, but using products such the ones listed here will leave a more organized and professional looking installation.

Lucent Technologies: HomeStar Wiring System

HomeStar is a complete home wiring solution. It has three basic system components: A central "service center" to connect all of the cabling technologies, distribution cables to the information outlets, and the information outlets themselves. The HomeStar system has provisions for telephone, data, CATV, home automation, and future technologies.

Siemon Co.: Home Cabling System

The Home Cabling System is Siemon's solution for organized residential cabling. It has two special components: the "CT Command Center," a distribution panel for all of the information technologies, and the "Max Designer Faceplate," an aesthetic information outlet. The Home Cabling System has provisions for telephone, data, CATV, and future technologies.

Leviton Telcom: Integrated Solutions for Home & Office

Leviton's distribution housing kits provide a modular solution for residential voice, data, and cable TV distribution. This kit consists of a distribution panel housing that holds modular cards. The technician then can decide exactly which modular cards the customer requires to fulfill their needs. Cards are also available that hold Leviton's QuickPort snap-in modules, so special needs such as fiber optic distribution are accommodated.

Private Branch Exchange (PBX) systems are phone switching systems. They allow people to dial between offices using extensions instead of full phone numbers. When you pick up a phone on a PBX system, you hear a fake dial tone. When you dial 9 (for most systems), the PBX switches the call onto an outside phone line.

An advantage of the PBX system is the ability to have more phone numbers than phone lines. For example, if a company has 200 employees, but believes that they will not use more than 100 lines at a time, then the company can set up the PBX system to switch 100 outside phone lines and 200 inside phone numbers. Then the company only has to pay the phone company for the 100 phone lines, and charges for the extra numbers.

The company also saves per-call charges because calls switched between two extensions on the same system are not switched onto the public telephone network.

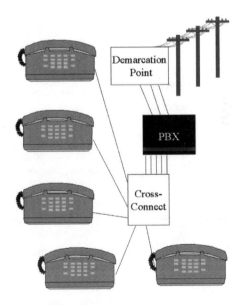

PBX Systems

Leased Lines & Multiplexing

Leased Lines

A "leased line" is a fixed amount of bandwidth that a customer leases from the *common carrier* (usually a phone company). The term leased line comes from situations in the past where a company would literally rent a pair of wires from the common carrier, but modern common carriers *multiplex* many customers' lines onto high-speed fiber optic cables.

Customers who want a leased line typically pay the common carrier a connection fee plus distance charges for the distance (usually by the meter) between the two ends of the link. The customer gets a connection with a constant amount of bandwidth available, 24 hours a day 7 days a week. There is no dial-up involved, because the line is set up point-to-point between the two sites. Leased lines are commonly used between businesses and Internet providers, and in these cases the customer is also charged a monthly connection fee from the Internet service provider.

Look on the next page for information on line speeds and names.

Multiplexing

Multiplexing is the combination of more than one signal into one signal for transfer over a line. A real world analogy of multiplexing is when you mail a letter to someone, the postman doesn't drive the letter to its destination, it is combined with many other letters on a bigger carrier.

Leased lines between two locations of one company commonly multiplex video, data and voice. For example, a company with one office in Virginia and another in California can lease a line between their offices to connect their LANs and avoid long distance phone charges by multiplexing data and conversations onto the same leased line. Multiplexing is also done by the phone company to combine thousands of phone conversations onto fiber optic cables.

When multiplexing data, the multiplexed line must be at least as fast as all of the lines being multiplexed onto it, combined.

Line Speeds

Analog Phone (POTS)

A simple analog phone line has a bandwidth of 64 kilobits per second for analog data. The fastest of modems (modulator/demodulators - they convert digital computer signals to analog signals) transmits data at 33.6 kbps onto the phone network. A transmission speed of up to approximately 53 kbps can be achieved through the sending end (usually an Internet Service Provider (ISP)) being hooked up to the digital phone network. Analog lines are sometimes called "plain old telephone service" or POTS.

ISDN

To make phone service more friendly for data, phone companies upgraded their equipment to handle digital phone lines, known as ISDN. These lines have the same 64 kbps bandwidth as analog phone lines, but ISDN lines are rated for digital data transfer. ISDN combines two "B" channels, each 64 kbps, to make a total available bandwidth of 128 kbps.

T-1/DS-1

Twenty four digital 64k channels are combined to make a T-1 (or DS-1 or Digital Signal-1) line, with a total bandwidth of 1.5436 megabits per second. This is typically a leased line service. T-1 lines are commonly run over two UTP pairs. Fractional T-1 lines are available, they have 1/2, 1/4 or another fraction of the bandwidth of a T-1 line.

T-2/DS-2

Four T-1 lines, or 6.312 mbps. These are uncommon.

T-3/DS-3

T3 lines carry 44.736 Mbps, or 672 phone channels. These lines are commonly used for ISPs to connect thousands of users from dial-up lines to the Internet. T-3 lines can run on a broadband carrier over coaxial cable, or on fiber optic cable.

OC-3

OC stands for Optical Carrier. It is an extremely high speed digital line, running at 155 mbps. These are mostly used by common carriers for high speed network communications, and by local telephone companies for multiplexing thousands of voice lines between the central office and a distribution site within a few miles of the end customer.

Appendix A
Contact Information

ADC (Component manufacturer)
12501 Clearwater Dr.
Minnetonka, MN 55343
(800) 366-3891
www.adc.com

Agilent Technologies Wirescope Division (Test equipment manufacturer)
753 Forest St.
Marlborough, MA 01752
(800) 418-7111
www.wirescope.com

AMP (Component manufacturer)
Harrisburg, PA 17105-3608
(800) 722-1111
www.amp.com

ANSI (American National Standards Institute)
11 W 42nd St
New York, NY 10036
(212) 642-4900
www.ansi.org

B-Line Systems, Inc. (Cable management products)
509 W Monroe St
Highland, IL 62249
(618) 654-2184
www.b-line.com

Belden Wire & Cable (Cable manufacturer)
2200 U. S. Highway 27 South
Richmond, IN 47374
(765) 983-5200
www.belden.com

Appendix A: Contact Information

Berk-Tek (Cable manufacturer)
132 White Oak Rd
New Holland, PA 17557
(800) 237-5835
www.berktek.com

BICSI, *A Telecommunications Association*
8610 Hidden River Parkway
Tampa, FL 33637-1000
(800) 242-7405
www.bicsi.org

Cabling Business (Trade magazine)
12035 Shiloh Rd., Suite 350
Dallas, Texas 75228-9601
(214) 328-1717
www.cablingbusiness.com

Cabling Installation & Maintenance Magazine
One Technology Park Dr.
Westford, MA 01886
Subscriptions: (918) 832-9349
www.cable-install.com

CommScope (Cable manufacturer)
1375 Lenior Rhyne Blvd.
Hickory, NC 28603
(800) 982-1708
www.commscope.com

Datacom Textron (Cable performance testers)
11001 31st Pl. W
Everett, WA 98204
(425) 355-0590
www.datacomtech.com

Communications Cabling

Appendix A: Contact Information

Electronic Industries Alliance (Standards organization)
2500 Wilson Blvd.
Arlington, VA 22201
(703) 907-7500
www.eia.org

Encore Enclosure Systems (Data cabinet manufacturer)
1344 North McKemy Ave. Bldg 2
Chandler, AZ 85226
(408) 705-5590
www.encoreusa.com

Fluke (Cable tester manufacturer)
PO Box 9090
Everett, WA 98206
(800) 443-5853
www.fluke.com/nettools

Global Engineering Documents (Distributor of standards copies)
15 Inverness Way East
Englewood, CO 80112
(800) 854-7179
global.ihs.com

Hubbell Premise Wiring (Component manufacturer)
14 Lords Hill Rd.
Stonington, CT 06378
(203) 535-8326
www.hubbell-premise.com

Homaco (Components manufacturer)
1875 W. Fullerton Ave.
Chicago, IL 60614
(888) 446-6226
www.homaco.com

Appendix A: Contact Information

Ideal Industries (Tool manufacturer)
Becker Pl.
Sycamore, IL 60178
(815) 895-5181
www.idealindustries.com

IEEE (Institute of Electrical and Electronics Engineers)
445 Hoes Ln.
Piscataway, NJ 08854
(800)-678-4333
www.ieee.org

Krone (Component manufacturer)
6950 South Tucson Way, Suite R
Englewood, CO 80012
(800) 775-5766
www.kroneamericas.com

Leviton Manufacturing Co., Inc.
59-23 Little Neck Pkwy
Little Neck, NY 11362
(800) 833-3532
www.leviton.com

Leviton Telcom (Components manufacturer)
2222 222nd St SE
Bothell, WA 98021-4422
(800) 722-2082
www.levitontelcom.com

Lucent Technologies (Cable & components manufacturer)
600 Mountain Ave
Murray Hill, NJ 07974
(888) 458-2368
www.lucent.com/systimax

Appendix A: Contact Information

MOD-TAP (Now owned by Molex Premises Networks)

Mohawk/CDT (Cable manufacturer)
9 Mohawk Dr.
Leominster, MA 01453
(978) 537-9961
www.mohawk-cdt.com

Molex (Component manufacturer)
8 Executive Dr.
Hudson, NH 03051
(800) 866-3827
www.molexpn.com

Nelson Firestop Products
4041 South Sheridan Rd
Tulsa, OK 74145
(800) 331-7325

Network World, Inc. (NetDraw Plus software)
161 Worcester Rd.
Farmingham, MA 01701
(800) 643-4668
www.netdraw.com

NFPA (National Fire Protection Association)
1 Batterymarch Park
Quincy, MA 02269-9101
(617) 770-3000
www.nfpa.org

NORDX/CDT (Cable & components manufacturer)
10 Mechanic St. 3rd Floor
Worcester, MA 01608
(800) 262-9334
www.nordx.com

Appendix A: Contact Information

Panduit (Component & raceway manufacturer)
17301 Ridgeland Ave.
Tinley Park, IL 60477-3091
(888) 506-5400
www.panduit.com

Platt (Tool case manufacturer)
4051 W. 51st St
Chicago, IL 60632
(800) 997-5288
www.plattcases.com

RBT Systems, Inc. (Cabling & fiber optic education)
PO Box 324
Round Hill, VA 20142
(540) 554-2465
www.rbtsystems.com

Rack Technologies (Communications racks and enclosures)
2217-F Distribution Center Dr.
Charlotte, NC 28269
(888) RACKTEK

Remee (Cable manufacturer)
468 Rt. 17A
Florida, NY 10921
(800) 431-3864
www.remee.com

Scope Communications (Now owned by Agilent Technologies)

The Siemon Company (Components manufacturer)
76 Westbury Park Rd
Watertown, CT 06795
(860) 274-2523
www.siemon.com

Communications Cabling

Appendix A: Contact Information

Stewart Connector (Connector manufacturer)
11118 Susquehanna Trail South
Glen Rock, PA 17327-9199
(717) 235-7512
www.stewartconnector.com

Superior Essex (Cable manufacturer)
150 Interstate North Pkwy.
Atlanta, GA 30339-2101
(800) 685-4887
www.superioressex.com

Superior Modular Products (Components manufacturer)
130-B Buckeye Cove Rd
Swannanoa, NC 28778
(828) 298-2260
www.superiormod.com

Telecommunications Industry Association (Standards organization)
2500 Wilson Boulevard, Suite 300
Arlington, VA 22201
(703) 907-7700
www.tiaonline.org

UNICOM (Components manufacturer)
908 Canada Ct.
City of Industry, CA 91748
(800) 346-6668
www.unicomlink.com

Wavetek Corporation (Cable tester manufacturer)
9045 Balboa Ave.
San Diego, CA 92123
(800) 854-2708
www.wavetek.com

Appendix B
Safety Information

Introduction

Every element of a work site is a potential safety hazard. The ladder you stand on can fall. You can trip over items left on the floor. People can be seriously injured if you drop a tool from a high place. You can drown in very shallow water in a manhole.

Installer Qualification

Before entering a job site, it is very important that a cabling technician:

√   Learn first aid procedures.

√   Become certified in CPR.

√   Understand their company's safety procedures.

√   Is familiar with local building codes and OSHA regulations for the job they are performing.

Words to Know
OSHA

Occupational Health and Safety Agency, a federal government agency that enforces laws related to worker safety. OSHA assigns large fines to businesses that violate safety laws.

Preparing the Work Area

It is very important to prepare a safe work area. People passing by can be injured by falling objects, touching live circuits left uncovered, or themselves falling into manholes or open floor panels. Installers can be seriously injured by people bumping into their ladders. If any work area accident occurs, it is generally considered the fault of the technician, because he or she is responsible for creating a safe work environment. The following safety rules will help you create a safe work environment:

√   When working outdoors, surround the area with bright warning tape to keep people from entering your work area.

√   Exercise extreme caution when working in wet or slippery areas.

√   When working in hallways within a building, make sure people can see your work area from far enough away so they can safely get around it. Do not place a ladder behind a door that can be opened.

√   Replace ceiling tiles once your work in that area is complete. Leaving unnecessary tiles open is unsafe and looks unprofessional.

√   Rope off areas around open floor panels and manholes.

√   Do not leave tools unattended. People have a tendency to "borrow" them.

√   Keep all tools and other items in a neat and orderly manner. The more scattered they are, the more likely someone will come by and trip over them.

Ladder Safety

Ladders are a dangerous but necessary part of cable installation. The first step of using a ladder safely is using the correct type.

Type	Advantages	Disadvantages
Wood	Non-Conductive. Inexpensive.	Very Heavy.
Aluminum	Inexpensive. Lighter than Wood.	Not Recommended since it is conductive.
Fiberglass	Non-Conductive. Very Lightweight.	Very Costly.

Before using a ladder, make sure it is in good condition. Make sure all of the rungs are tightly fastened to the side rails. Make sure the ladder is clean and the rungs are free from any slippery material. All ladders must be OSHA approved.

Place the ladder on a solid, flat floor. Do not place the ladder where it might be knocked over by a door opening or someone rounding a corner quickly. Make sure step ladders are fully opened and the middle support locked down.

Before using the ladder, read all of the safety messages printed on it. Observe the maximum weight rating. Do not stand on the top or second to top rung of the ladder. Many ladders have holes or cutouts for tools on the top. Use these to avoid dropping tools. Keep a scrap wire box or bag to put scraps in, do not just drop anything. Do not leave tools on top of ladders you are not on.

If the job requires a ladder, use one! Do not stand on furniture or anything else not designed to hold people.

Using Tools & Avoiding Asbestos

Only use hand tools that are in good condition. Remember that you are far more likely to get cut from a dull blade than a sharp one. If a tool's handle is loose or damaged, it might break off, possibly causing serious injury.

√ Always cut away from your body, never towards yourself (or your other hand).

√ Use the correct tool for the job. If you do not know what the proper tool is to do the job, ask someone who knows.

√ Never cut off the grounding prong from grounded power tools. Do not use tools that have the grounding prong cut off.

√ Always read the instructions before using power tools or equipment. Always get training on tools you do not know how to use.

√ Use extreme caution when blindly drilling or sawing into anything.

Avoiding Asbestos

Asbestos causes many health problems. It is linked to cancer of the bronchial tubes, cancer of the chest and abdomen, and shortness of breath. Cancer risks are multiplied when asbestos inhalation is combined with smoking. The danger of asbestos lies with long, tiny fibers that can become airborne and inhaled. These fibers can collect in the lungs. Many symptoms of asbestos inhalation take years to show up.

Areas containing asbestos must be well marked with safety warnings and the building manager should have records of where asbestos exists. Asbestos in buildings must be properly wrapped to prevent fibers from becoming airborne. Disturbing installations by sawing, drilling or moving asbestos can set fibers airborne and result in a serious breathing hazard.

Protective Equipment

Protective equipment, when used correctly, significantly reduces the chance of getting injured while on the job. Before you use safety equipment, inspect it for damage or defects. Listed below are common types of protective equipment:

Headgear

Also called hard-hats, you must wear one any time you are in an area that there is a danger of electric shock, falling objects, or flying objects. Make sure the hat fits properly and does not fall off or block your vision. Do not use a metal hard-hat. Remember that OSHA often fines businesses for violating this law.

Goggles/Glasses

You must wear goggles or safety glasses any place where there is a danger to the eyes, including, but not limited to: working with power tools, batteries, or optical fiber. Make sure the glasses or goggles are ANSI/OSHA approved and provide side protection. Prescription glasses or sunglasses never take the place of proper eye protection, however special prescription safety glasses are available.

Gloves

Gloves must be worn when you work with hazardous chemicals, high voltages, extreme temperatures, or sharp objects. Do not handle high voltage, extreme temperatures or dangerous chemicals unless you are thoroughly trained in their handing and safety procedures.

Breathing Protection

Must be worn when any harmful vapor or gas is in the area. Become intensely familiar with OSHA laws and equipment usage before using breathing protection or entering a hazardous areas. Breathing some harmful gasses or vapors can very quickly knock you unconscious and kill you.

Protective Equip. & Dressing Safely

Safety Harness

Must be worn whenever installers are in high places, and often in manholes. Before climbing higher than you would on a step ladder, or entering a manhole, become familiar with OSHA laws for such work. Safety harnesses must also be worn when using lifts and while working on power poles.

Lifting Belts and Ear Protection

Wear these when the situations require them.

Dressing Safely

Apparel

Many companies provide uniforms or company shirts to their employees. Wear clothing that is not baggy enough to get caught on machinery or impede your movement.

Hair

Keep your hair trimmed or tied back. Remember professionalism in addition to safety when choosing a hair style.

Shoes

Do not wear sneakers or tennis shoes. OSHA requires steel toed boots in many situations. Keep your shoes tied.

Jewelry

Do not wear rings, earrings or other jewelry that can get caught on, or short out anything.

Lightning

Be aware of your surroundings during electrical storms.

High Areas

Never throw or drop anything down from high areas.

Pushing Fish Tape

(Through Conduits) Never push metal fish tape through conduits if you are not sure of its exit point. Many conduits end straight into high voltage areas of electrical panels.

Manholes

A complete set of regulations apply for working in manholes or underground cable vaults. Become familiar with all of these laws before entering such an area.

Optical Fibers (Fiber Optics)

Never look into the end of a fiber. Intense lasers used to transmit data can quickly leave you blind. If you see scraps of fibers anywhere, immediately get a qualified person to clean them up. Fiber can easily enter the skin and in some cases requires surgery to remove.

Chemicals

Always get training on the use of chemicals before using them. Read the MSDS (Material Safety Data Sheet) if you need information on the safe handling and hazards of a chemical. Never smoke in the presence of chemicals.

Appendix C
Telecommunications Closet Diagram

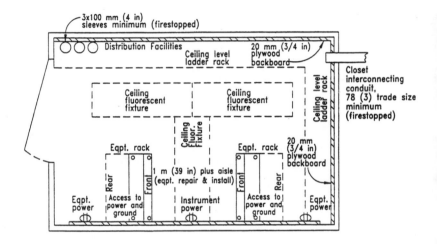

This diagram, entitled "Typical Telecommunications Closet," is Figure 7.2-2 in the ANSI/EIA/TIA-569-A standards. It is reprinted with permission from the Telecommunications Industry Association. Contact Global Engineering Documents for a complete copy of the standard.

Appendix D
Infrastructure Symbols

Cable Symbols

Cable/Wire (denote type)

Cable to be removed.

Cable slack (denote slack length)

Termination Symbols

Termination hardware, not protected (denote terminal size)

X_A

Cross-connect hardware (denote description, if applicable)

Grounding/Bonding Symbols

Connection to ground (conductor size noted)

Pathway Symbols

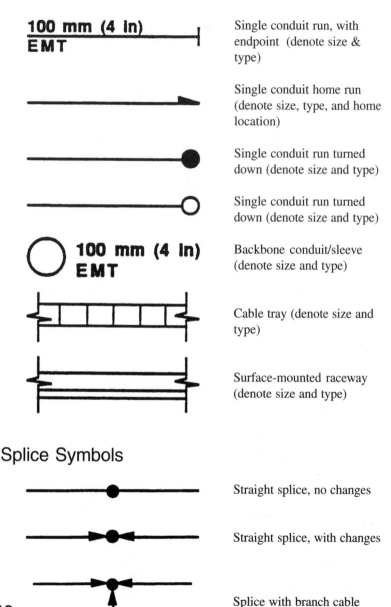

100 mm (4 in)
EMT

Single conduit run, with endpoint (denote size & type)

Single conduit home run (denote size, type, and home location)

Single conduit run turned down (denote size and type)

Single conduit run turned down (denote size and type)

100 mm (4 in)
EMT

Backbone conduit/sleeve (denote size and type)

Cable tray (denote size and type)

Surface-mounted raceway (denote size and type)

Splice Symbols

Straight splice, no changes

Straight splice, with changes

Splice with branch cable

Space Symbols

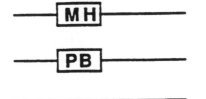

Manhole (denote dimensions)

Pull Box (denote dimensions)

Backboard (denote dimensions

NAME

Telecommunications space (denote dimensions)

Miscellaneous Symbols

Wall-mounted telecom outlet box/connector

Floor-mounted telecom outlet box/connector

Ceiling-mounted telecom outlet box/connector

For telecom outlets denote type, size, configuration, and descriptive information as required.

Equipment Rack (show to scale)

Equipment Cabinet (show to scale)

This is only a summary of symbols applicable to this book. For a complete listing of infrastructure symbols, consult the ANSI/TIA/EIA-606 standard. Information reprinted with permission from the Telecommunications Industry Association.

Appendix E
Acronym Dictionary

AC	Alternating Current
ACR	Attenuation to Crosstalk Ratio
ADSL	Asymmetric Digital Subscriber Line
ANSI	American National Standards Institute
ATM	Asynchronous Transfer Mode
AUI	Attachment Unit Interface
AWG	American Wire Gauge
BALUN	Balanced/Unbalanced
BICSI	Building Industry Consulting Services International
BNC	Bayonet-Neill-Concelman
CAN	Campus Area Network
CATV	Community Antenna Television
CCTV	Closed Circuit Television
CM	Communication Cable (NEC rating)
CMR	Communications Riser Cable (NEC rating)
CMP	Communications Plenum Cable (NEC rating)
CO	Central Office
CSA	Canadian Standards Association
CSMA/CD	Carrier Sense, Multiple Access, Collision Detect
dB	Decibels
DC	Direct Current
DS	Digital Signal
DSL	Digital Subscriber Line
DTMF	Dual Tone Multiple Frequency
EIA	Electronic Industries Alliance
ELFEXT	Equal Level Far End Crosstalk
EMI	Electro-Magnetic Interference
EMT	Electrical Metallic Tubing
ER	Equipment Room
FCC	Federal Communications Commission
FDDI	Fiber Distributed Data Interface
FEP	Fluorinated Ethylene Propylene
FEXT	Far End Crosstalk
FTP	Foiled Twisted Pair

GSA	General Services Administration
HVAC	Heating, Ventilation, Air Conditioning
IC	Intermediate Cross-Connect
IDC	Insulation Displacement Connector
IEEE	Institute of Electrical & Electronics Engineers
ISDN	Integrated Services Digital Network
ISO	International Organization for Standardization
ISP	Internet Service Provider
LAN	Local Area Network
MAN	Metropolitan Area Network
MAU	Multistation Access Unit
Mbps	Megabits Per Second
MBps	Megabytes Per Second
MC	Main Cross-connect
MHz	Megahertz
MP	Multipurpose Cable (NEC rating)
MPP	Multipurpose Plenum Cable (NEC rating)
MPR	Multipurpose Riser Cable (NEC rating)
MUX	Multiplex
NEC	National Electrical Code
NEMA	National Electrical Manufacturers Association
NEXT	Near End Crosstalk
NFPA	National Fire Protection Association
NIC	Network Interface Card
NM	Non-Metallic
NOS	Network Operating System
NTIS	National Technical Information Service
OC	Optical Carrier
OSHA	Occupational Safety & Health Administration
OSI	Open Systems Interconnection
PABX	Private Automated Branch Exchange
PBX	Private Branch Exchange
PDS	Premises Distribution System
POTS	Plain Old Telephone Service
PSACR	Power Sum Attenuation to Crosstalk Ratio
PSELFEXT	Power Sum Equal Level Far End Crosstalk
PSNEXT	Power Sum Near End Crosstalk
PSTN	Public Switched Telephone Network
PVC	Polyvinyl Chloride
RBOC	Regional Bell Operating Company

RCDD	Registered Communications Distribution Designer
RF	Radio Frequency
RFI	Radio Frequency Interference
RJ	Registered Jack
RUS	Rural Utilities Service
ScTP	Screened Twisted Pair
SNMP	Simple Network Management Protocol
SNR	Signal to Noise Ratio
SONET	Synchronous Optical Network
STP	Shielded Twisted Pair
TC	Telecommunications Closet
TCP/IP	Transmission Control Protocol/Internet Protocol
TDR	Time Domain Reflectometer
TGB	Telecommunications Grounding Busbar
TIA	Telecommunications Industry Association
TP	Twisted Pair
TP-PMD	Twisted Pair-Physical Medium Dependent
TSB	Telecommunications Systems Bulletin
UDC	Universal Data Connector
UL	Underwriters' Laboratories
USOC	Universal Service Ordering Code
UTP	Unshielded Twisted Pair
WAN	Wide Area Network
WAO	Work Area Outlet

Appendix F
FCC Order for Cat 3

On January 10, 2000, the FCC released an order altering its regulation concerning inside wiring in residences. The FCC has the authority to regulate anything, including wiring, that connects to the public telephone network. BICSI, along with other industry organizations, petitioned the FCC to require quality standards for inside wiring. This order became effective July 8, 2000. The full text of the order can be found on the www.fcc.gov website, however the summary of the legal amendment is reprinted here.

Title 47 of the Code of Federal Regulations Part 68 is amended as follows:

Part 68 - CONNECTION OF TERMINAL EQUIPMENT TO THE TELE-PHONE NETWORK

1. The authority citation for Part 68 continues to read as follows:

AUTHORITY: Sections 1, 4, 5, 201-5, 208, 215, 218, 226, 227, 303, 313, 314, 403, 404, 410, 522 of the Communications Act of 1934, as amended, 47 U.S.C. §§ 151, 154, 155, 201-5, 208, 215, 218, 226, 227, 303, 313, 314, 403, 404, 410, 522.

2. Section 68.213 is amended by revising paragraph (c) as follows:

§ 68.213 Installation of other than "fully protected" non-system simple customer premises wiring.

(c) <u>Material requirements</u>.

(1) For new installations and modifications to existing installations, copper conductors shall be, at a minimum, solid, 24 gauge or larger, twisted pairs that comply with the electrical specifications for Category 3, as defined in the ANSI EIA/TIA Building Wiring Standards.

(2) Conductors shall have insulation with a 1500 Volt rms minimum breakdown rating. This rating shall be established by covering the jacket or sheath with at least 15 cm (6 inches) (measured linearly on the cable) of conductive foil, and establishing a potential difference between the foil and all of the individual conductors connected together, such potential difference gradually increased over a 30 second time period to 1500 Volts rms, 60 Hertz, then applied continuously for one minute. At no time during this 90 second time interval shall the current between these points exceed 10 milliamperes peak.

(3) All wire and connectors meeting the requirements set forth in subparagraphs (1) and (2) above shall be marked, in a manner visible to the consumer, with the symbol "CAT 3" or a symbol consisting of a "C" with a "3" contained within the "C" character, at intervals not to exceed one foot (12 inches) along the length of the wire.

Appendix G
Further Reading

The following publications can be purchased from their respective publishers, refer to Appendix A for contact information:

Leviton Telcom, *Voice & Data Wiring Strategies*, 1998.

NFPA, *National Electrical Code*, 1999 (Every installer should carry a copy of this book. Also strongly recommended is the *National Electrical Code Handbook*, 1999)

TIA, *TIA/EIA Building Telecommunications Wiring Standards*, Global Engineering Documents, 1990-1996

The following books are commercially available through most bookstores:

Donald J. Sterling Jr., *Premises Cabling*, Delmar Publishers, 1995

The following and many other books are available from Telecom Books, at 1-800-LIBRARY:

Harry Newton, *Newton's Telecom Dictionary*, Flatiron Publishing, 1998

On the Internet:

Usenet newsgroup: comp.dcom.cabling
Cross-Connect Online: http://www.onepassinfo.com
Refer to companies' websites in Appendix A, many of them contain valuable information.

Numbers

GLOSSARY

10Base-2 10 Megabits per second, baseband Ethernet transmission over thin coaxial (RG-58) cable.

10Base-5 10 Megabits per second, baseband Ethernet transmission over thick coaxial (RG-8) cable.

10Base-T 10 Megabits per second, baseband Ethernet transmission over twisted pair (Cat 3 or better) cable.

802.3 IEEE designation for a CSMA/CD protocol (Otherwise known as Ethernet).

A

ACTIVE DEVICE Any device that has an external source of power for the purpose of altering or boosting data signals. Examples include repeaters, PBXs and computers.

AMERICAN NATIONAL STANDARDS INSTITUTE (ANSI) A standards organization. Its standards are highly respected in US industries. Standards are voluntary, but met due to industry demand.

AMERICAN STANDARD CODE FOR INFORMATION INTER-CHANGE (ASCII) A code used to decode numbers & 1/0 (binary) values into readable characters.

AMERICAN WIRE GAUGE (AWG) Standard measuring system for electrical conductors. A lower number is a larger diameter conductor.

APPLETALK A low speed, proprietary network designed to be used between Apple Computer Inc. computers and compatible peripherals. Appletalk is one of the few networks that can operate over quad (non-twisted) wire.

ASYNCHRONOUS TRANSFER MODE (ATM) A networking protocol. ATM splits voice, data and video information into small packets of data to increase the efficiency of transmission over long distance cable runs.

ATTACHMENT UNIT INTERFACE (**AUI**) A 15 pin D-shape connector available on many network interface cards and hubs. The AUI connector is usually used on thick Ethernet transceivers.

ATTENUATION The decrease of the power of a signal, light wave or light beam. Measured in decibels (loss of).

B

BACKBONE The wiring between equipment rooms/telecommunication closets. Backbone cabling carries the information of more than one end user.

BALANCED PAIR Two conductors, usually twisted around each other, carrying electrical inverse signals for the purpose of canceling out crosstalk.

BALANCED/UNBALANCED (**BALUN**) An adapter that is used to connect coaxial cable and twisted pair cable. It balances signals on the twisted pair side and unbalances signals for the coaxial.

BANDWIDTH The range of frequencies available for data transfer with minimal distortion in a cable, measured in hertz (Hz).

BEND RADIUS The maximum bend a cable can tolerate without damaging the cable or impeding performance.

BAYONET-NEILL-CONCELMAN (**BNC**) **CONNECTOR** A metal locking connector used with thin coaxial (RG-58) cable.

C

CATEGORY 3,4,5 Cable and connectors that meet the standards outlined for their category according to the TIA/EIA-568-A standard. All new installations should use Category 5 cabling and connectors.

G
L
O
S
S
A
R
Y

CENTRAL OFFICE (CO) A telephone company office where phone calls are switched and distributed.

CHANNEL The entire cable run (including patch cords, connectors, cross-connects, and cable) between two pieces of equipment (such as between a computer and a hub).

COAXIAL CABLE (Coax) A cable that is composed of a center conductor, an insulated layer (called a dielectric), a braid around the dielectric, and then a jacket around it all.

CONDUCTOR A material that provides a low impedance path for electrical current.

CONDUIT A type of pipe used for housing cable runs.

CONTINUITY A continuous path for electrical current to flow from one point to another.

CROSS-CONNECT Also known as punch block or patch panel. An organized method of splicing cables. A cross-connect is a passive device, as it is only a connection point for cables.

CROSS-TALK See Near End Cross-Talk

D

DAISY CHAIN A method for connecting equipment mostly found in older buildings and homes. Equipment is connected with a cable run between each station. This method is not recommended since a break in any part of the cable can disable either the whole system or the equipment past the break.

DECIBEL (dB) The measure of the change in signal strength. An increase of 3 decibels is a 100% increase in signal strength.

DEMARCATION POINT The point of connection between the public telephone network and building cabling. Although the demarcation point is located on the customer's property, only the phone company can service the cabling on their side of the demarcation point.

DRAIN WIRE   A bare conductor in STP and ScTP cable running along with the shield. It is used to terminate or ground the shield.

DROP   Slang for a cable run, in the star topology.

DROP CABLE   Usually used in the Linear Bus Topology, a cable that connects a work area outlet to the bus cable.

DUAL TONE MULTIPLE FREQUENCY (DTMF)
Numbers or symbols are encoded in tones to communicate information across telephone lines.

E

ELECTRONIC INDUSTRIES ALLIANCE (EIA)   An organization that publishes electronic industry standards.

ELECTROMAGNETIC INTERFERENCE (EMI)   The interference caused in communication lines by magnetic fields.

ETHERNET   A local area network protocol. Ethernet is the most widely used network protocol, and can run over a wide range cabling types. Also see Fast Ethernet

F

FAST ETHERNET   Ethernet that transmits at 100 Megabits per second over CAT 5 or fiber optic cable.

FIBER DISTRIBUTED DATA INTERFACE (FDDI)   FDDI runs at 100 Mbps over fiber optic cable, in the ring topology.

FIRESTOP   A putty, caulk, sleeve or other method used to stop flame, gas & water spread through openings. Most local building codes require firestop to be installed to seal any penetrations through firewalls or fire barriers.

FREQUENCY   The rate at which an electrical signal fluctuates. Measured in Hertz (Hz).

GLOSSARY

171

FULL DUPLEX Two devices communicating with each other simultaneously over one cabling run.

H

HALF DUPLEX A connection between two devices that can carry information in both directions, but only one direction at a time.

HOME RUN A term sometimes used to describe a run from a station all the way back to the wiring closet.

HUB A wiring device used in the star topology to connect cables between stations. Active hubs also amplify signals.

HYBRID CONNECTOR A connector providing a connection for multiple cable types.

I

INDUCTION Whenever electricity flows through a conductor, a magnetic field is created. This magnetic field can be picked up by nearby conductors, reducing signal quality.

INSULATION DISPLACEMENT CONNECTOR (IDC) A wire termination that does not require the installer to strip the insulation off of the conductor. A metal clip slices through the insulation and makes a connection to the conductor.

INTERMEDIATE DISTRIBUTION FRAME (IDF) An intermediate cross-connect between the main distribution frame and the telecom closet.

INSTITUTE OF ELECTRICAL AND ELECTRONIC ENGINEERS (IEEE) A standards organizations, publishes some standards for networks such as the 802.x series.

IMPEDANCE The total opposition to the flow of current in a conductor.

INTEGRATED SERVICES DIGITAL NETWORK (ISDN) A public phone service with higher quality phone lines that are better suited for digital data transfer.

J

JACK   A receptacle for a plug. A jack refers to the female end of the connector.

JACKET   The outer insulation of a cable, commonly made out of PVC, Teflon FEP, or other plastic.

K

KEYED (Modular Jack or Plug)   Keyed jacks and plugs have matching bumps that are specifically made to match up with each other. Keyed jacks & plugs are made so incompatible modular outlets and cables can not be connected.

L

LEGACY APPLICATION   A cabling or network system that is no longer widely supported, but a customer has such a large installation of it that they do not want to update their technology. Examples often include ARCnet and DECnet systems.

LINK   A cable run between two points. For example, the cable between a work area outlet and a cross-connect is known as a link. Compare with channel.

LOCAL AREA NETWORK (**LAN**)   A network within a single office area. It can be a part of a wide area network (WAN).

M

MEDIA ACCESS UNIT (**MAU**)   An Ethernet transceiver. Used to be a Token Ring networking term, but that equipment is mostly referred to as an MSAU.

MEGABITS PER SECOND (**Mbps**)   Approx. one million bits (binary 1/0's) of data transferred per second.

MEGABYTES PER SECOND (**MBPS**) Approx. one million bytes (approx. 8 million bits) of data transferred per second.

MAIN DISTRIBUTION FRAME (MDF) The central cross-connect of the cabling system. It is the top of the cabling distribution hierarchy.

MEGAHERTZ (MHz) One million cycles per second (hertz).

MODIFIED MODULAR JACK (MMJ) A Digital Equipment Corp. (DEC) jack that has 6 wires and is keyed on the right side. This is used in the DEC Wiring System.

MULTI-STATION ACCESS UNIT (MSAU) A central connection point (hub) for Token Ring network cables.

N

NATIONAL ELECTRICAL CODE (NEC) A standard (NFPA-70) published by the National Fire Protection Association (NFPA). Although the NEC itself is not a law, many local governments adopt all or part of it as a building code.

NEAR END CROSSTALK (NEXT) Stray signals inducting between pairs of a cable. Improper terminations and cable damage can cause excessive crosstalk.

NODE A device that is actively connected to the network.

O

OPEN The lack of continuity in a conductor or a cable.

P

PAIR Two conductors of a cable. They usually carry balanced signals and should be twisted around each other. See *Balanced Pair.*

PATCH CORDS A connection between outlets. There are patch cords between cross-connect blocks and hubs, between two cross-connects, and between a work area outlet and equipment.

PATCH PANEL A type of cross-connect that features a punch-down block connected to a jack.

PLENUM A chamber that houses environmental air transfer. Plenum rated cables are required anywhere that environmental air is transferred, including above some drop ceilings and under some computer room floors.

POLYVINYL CHLORIDE (PVC) A type of plastic commonly used in non-plenum rated cable jackets.

PRIVATE BRANCH EXCHANGE (PBX) A private phone switching system.

Q

QUAD WIRE Four conductor, non-twisted cable that is common in older residential installations. The new installation of quad wire in residences became illegal on July 8, 2000.

R

RACEWAY A plastic or metal enclosure for routing cable, usually used for safety and aesthetic reasons

RETURN LOSS A ratio, measured in decibels, of the original power sent in a signal and the power returned.

REGISTERED JACK (RJ) The FCC-assigned numbers for specific data outlets & applications.

RESISTANCE Measured in OHMs, it is the opposition to the flow of DC current.

RISER CABLE A cable that is used between different stories of a building.

S

SEGMENT A section of a network. The maximum length of cabling systems is usually measured in maximum segment length. Segments can be split up by bridges, routers, and certain other network devices.

SERVICE LOOP   Extra cable left behind a wall plate to provide slack for later changes.

SIMPLEX   A system only designed to transmit data in one direction.

SOLID CABLE   Conductors made of a single wire as opposed to many strands. Used in permanent cabling runs.

SPLICE   A connection of two different cables made by bonding each conductor.

SPUDGER   A tool, with a hook on the end, that is commonly used to pull conductors off of 66-type cross-connects

STRANDED CABLE   A cable made up of many small strands of conductors as opposed to one solid conductor.

T

T1   A North American standard for leased line data communication. Has a speed of 1.54 Megabits per second.

TELECOMMUNICATIONS INDUSTRY ASSOCIATION (TIA) A standards organization that creates standards related to telecommunications, including TIA/EIA-568-A.

TERMINATE   To install a connector on the end of a cable.

TERMINATION   The connector or terminal that is bonded to the end of a cable.

THIN COAXIAL   RG-58 coaxial cable used in 10Base-2 networks.

THICK COAXIAL   RG-8 coaxial cable used in 10Base-5 networks.

TOKEN RING   A LAN protocol that at one time competed with Ethernet, but at this time its popularity is waning.

TOPOLOGY The physical placement and configuration of network cables and equipment.

TWISTED PAIR CABLE Two insulated conductors, twisted around each other with a consistent length of each twist. The twist length is calculated to minimize the crosstalk between pairs. Most twisted pair cable has four pairs (8 conductors).

W

WORK AREA OUTLET The jack (usually wall mounted) that gives network or phone access to the work area.

Index

Symbols

100 Pair UTP 13
100+ Pair Color Codes 189
100Base-T 72, 73
100VG-AnyLAN 105
10Base-2 76, 77
10Base-5 74, 75
10Base-T 72, 73, 82
110 Connector 43
110 Cross-connect 15, 46
110 cross-connect 44, 52
110 Jack 15, 48
110 Patch Panel 15, 54
25 Pair Color Codes 187
4 Pair Colors 185
66 Clip 43
66 Cross-connect 15, 47, 56
66M/66B 47

A

AMP modular plugs 23
Amp Tap 75
ANSI 102
Attenuation Test 95
Autotest 95

B

Backbone Cabling 46
Bend Radius 121
BICSI 102
Binder groups 189
BIX 43
BNC 14, 66, 77

Bonding 29
Braid 60

C

Cable Distances 110
Cable ID strip 45, 46
Cable management 125
Cable TV 59
Cabling System 99
Capacitance 88
Category 24
Category 3 24, 73
Category 5 24, 73
Category 5E 24, 73
CATV 59
CCTV 59
Center conductor 60
Channel 41
Characteristic impedance 88
CM/CMR/CMP 115
Coaxial 13
Coaxial Cable 77
Coaxial cable types 60
Collision domain 82
Color code 185
Conductor 11
Conductor Size 25
Conduit 126
Connector block 44, 46
Continuity 33
Continuity Tester 18
Crimp die 17
Crimp sleeve 60
Crimp tool 17
Cross-connect 41
Crossover cable 85
CSMA/CD 80, 105

D

Data Rate 90
Demarcation Point 131

179

Notes

Notes

Color Codes

Tip & Ring

Modern phone and network cabling is based on four pairs of two conductors: the **tip** and **ring**. The exact markings of the ring and tip vary between manufacturers, but the ring always is dominantly colored while the tip is dominantly white (white for pairs 1-5, more on this on page 185).

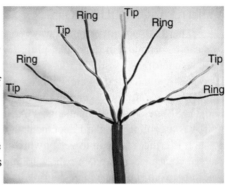

4 Pair Colors

The most widely used cable is four pair UTP. The four pair color code is at right.

Pair 1 Blue

Pair 2 Orange

Pair 3 Green

Pair 4 Brown

To help you remember the four pair color code, imagine sitting in a park in a warm, sunny day. You look up, and from top to bottom you see the blue sky, orange sun, green grass and brown dirt.

Wiring Configurations

There are several different ways conductors can be arranged in a modular plug. Two were standardized by article 10.4.5 of the TIA/EIA-568-A standard, they are T568A and T568B. Be careful not to confuse terms: T568A and T568B are color arrangements; TIA/EIA-568-A is a cabling standard document.

It is critical for you to verify which wiring pattern your jacks and patch panels are made for. It also helps to run a test after the first installed cable to make sure your patterns are correct.

The USOC (Universal Service Ordering Code) patterns are used in many phone cabling installations. When you perform service on a system cabled with USOC make sure you identify the correct pattern.

In some cases, you will find a modified USOC pattern that has a reversed pair 4. It is sometimes called *Generic USOC*. This is common in older installations, before the FCC standardized the RJ-61X configuration.

Most new data installations use the T568B pattern. The T568A configuration is popular in government, military, and foreign installations. USOC is common with phone systems, but it is not specified in TIA/EIA-568-A. USOC is used for two, four, and six position phone jacks simply by omitting the outside pairs.

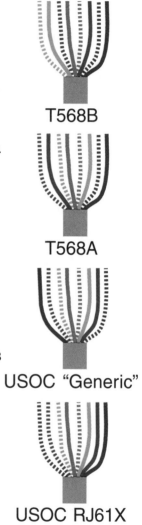

T568B

T568A

USOC "Generic"

USOC RJ61X

25 Pair Color Codes

The four pair color code, as shown earlier in this book, is a subset of the 25+ pair color code. In the four pair color code, there were four colors applied to the rings, and the tip was white.

The 25+ pair color code adds a new ring color, for pair five, slate. One way to remember the ring colors is <u>B</u>ell <u>O</u>perators <u>G</u>ive <u>B</u>etter <u>S</u>ervice (Blue, Orange, Green, Brown, Slate).

The pairs over pair five have a different colored tip conductor than white. The appropriate colors are shown to the right.

For example, if you were trying to figure out what yellow-green is, first you would find yellow is 16-20. Then you see green is #3, and yellow is the tip color, so yellow-green is pair 18 tip.

For the tip conductor, you can use <u>W</u>hy <u>R</u>un <u>B</u>ackwards <u>Y</u>ou'll <u>V</u>omit.

Pair 1 Ring Blue
Pair 2 Ring Orange
Pair 3 Ring Green
Pair 4 Ring Brown
Pair 5 Ring Slate

Pairs 1-5 Tip White
Pairs 6-10 Tip Red
Pairs 11-15 Tip Black
Pairs 16-20 Tip Yellow
Pairs 21-25 Tip Violet

	Tip Color	Ring Color
Pair 1	**White/Blue**	**Blue/White**
Pair 2	**White/Orange**	**Orange/White**
Pair 3	**White/Green**	**Green/White**
Pair 4	**White/Brown**	**Brown/White**
Pair 5	**White/Slate**	**Slate/White**
Pair 6	**Red/Blue**	**Blue/Red**
Pair 7	**Red/Orange**	**Orange/Red**

25 Pair Color Codes

	Tip Color	Ring Color	
Pair 8	Red/Green	Green/Red	
Pair 9	Red/Brown	Brown/Red	
Pair 10	Red/Slate	Slate/Red	
Pair 11	Black/Blue	Blue/Black	
Pair 12	Black/Orange	Orange/Black	
Pair 13	Black/Green	Green/Black	
Pair 14	Black/Brown	Brown/Black	
Pair 15	Black/Slate	Slate/Black	
Pair 16	Yellow/Blue	Blue/Yellow	
Pair 17	Yellow/Orange	Orange/Yellow	
Pair 18	Yellow/Green	Green/Yellow	
Pair 19	Yellow/Brown	Brown/Yellow	
Pair 20	Yellow/Slate	Slate/Yellow	
Pair 21	Violet/Blue	Blue/Violet	
Pair 22	Violet/Orange	Orange/Violet	
Pair 23	Violet/Green	Green/Violet	
Pair 24	Violet/Brown	Brown/Violet	
Pair 25	Violet/Slate	Slate/Violet	

100+ Pair Color Codes

100 Pair cables have four identical groups of 25 pairs, but they have strings wrapped around each group of 25 pairs in the cable. The groups of 25 pairs are called "binder groups". For 100 pair cable, the four string colors are blue, orange, green and brown, and the order is the same as the conductor color codes: Blue: Pairs 1-25; Orange: Pairs 26-50; Green: Pairs 51-75; Brown: Pairs 76-100.

Some cables have two color strings wrapped around each binder group. The colored strings then follow the same ordering as the pairs on pages 187 and 188. For example a binder group with a black/green string around it consists of pairs 301-325.

Notice the strings wrapped around each binder group:

Identifying Continuity Faults

Pictures below are based on T568B. Pay attention to the order of the pairs & the tip/ring.

T568B Configuration

**Short Pair 2 Tip &
Pair 2 Ring**

Open Pair 2 Ring

**Miswire Pair 3 Tip &
Pair 4 Tip**

Reversed Pair 2

**Transposed Pair 1 &
Pair 3**

Communications Cabling

Split Pairs

In a split pair, there is continuity on a cable, but the pairs don't match up correctly. A miswire of the same type on both ends will result in continuity, but since then the pairs are not twisted together correctly it yields the signal quality of untwisted cable.

You might be wondering, "if there is continuity, isn't that all it needs?" The reason a cable has pair twists in the first place is so when the equipment applies balanced signals to the cable, the pairs are twisted so the balanced signals cancel out each others' interference.

A related consideration about choosing termination configuration is system requirements. If a system transmits balanced signals on pins 1 and 2, a T568A or T568B cable is needed. If you plugged a RJ61X-terminated cable into such a system, you will be transmitting balanced signals on the tip of pair 4 and the tip of pair 3. If it is a lower speed system, this may work, but higher speed systems will fail. It cancels the whole advantage of twisted pair cabling.

Correct T568B
Configuration

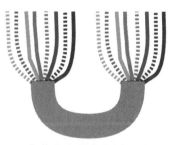

Split Pair Pair 2 Ring &
Pair 3 Tip

In the above example, the pins are all connected straight through between both ends. But since the conductors are not in their correct places, it has a split pair, and will fail wiremap testing by performance testers and most continuity testers.

Telephone Cabling Color Codes

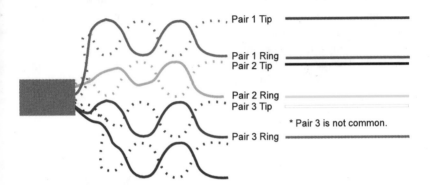

Pair 1 Tip

Pair 1 Ring
Pair 2 Tip

Pair 2 Ring
Pair 3 Tip

* Pair 3 is not common.

Pair 3 Ring